My Pious Friends and Drunken Companions

and

More Pious Friends and Drunken Companions

"THE FACE UPON THE FLOOR"

WITH ONE MORE STROKE TO THE SHAPELY HEAD
HE FELL ACROSS THE PICTURE —— DEAD.

AN ENGRAVING BY JOHN HELD JR INCLUDED IN HIS
THESIS AMERICANA.

My Pious Friends and Drunken Companions

and

More Pious Friends and Drunken Companions

Songs and Ballads of Conviviality Collected by
FRANK SHAY

Magnificently Illuminated by
JOHN HELD JR.

Dover Publications, Inc., New York

Published in the United Kingdom by Constable and
Company Limited, 10 Orange Street, London W.C.2.

This new Dover edition, first published in 1961, is
an unabridged republication of the text of the
following works:
My Pious Friends and Drunken Companions as
originally published by The Macaulay Company in
1927.
More Pious Friends and Drunken Companions as
originally published by The Macaulay Company in
1928.

The illustrations for this edition have been selected
from among those in the first editions.

This edition designed by Bernard Etter

Library of Congress Catalog Card Number: 61-66216

Manufactured in the United States of America

Dover Publications, Inc.
180 Varick Street
New York 14, N.Y.

Contents

MY PIOUS FRIENDS
AND DRUNKEN COMPANIONS

MORE PIOUS FRIENDS
AND DRUNKEN COMPANIONS

MY PIOUS FRIENDS

AND

DRUNKEN COMPANIONS

SONGS AND
BALLADS OF
CONVIVIALITY
Collected by
FRANK SHAY

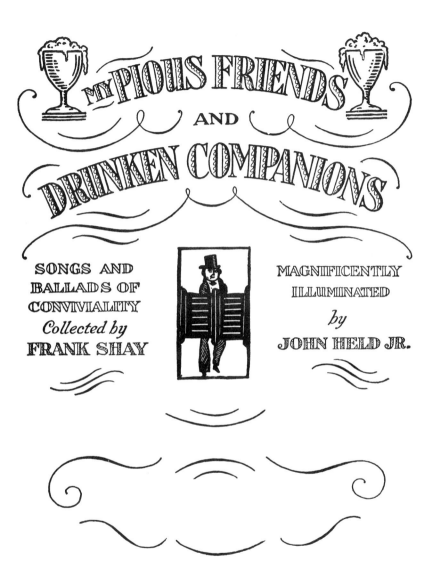

MAGNIFICENTLY
ILLUMINATED
by
JOHN HELD JR.

"Pure water is the best of
    gifts that man to man can bring.
But who am I that I should have
    the best of anything?
Let princes revel at the pump,
    let peers with ponds make free,
Whiskey or wine, or even beer,
    is good enough for me."

                    Neaves.

Over the Burning Sands

All Americans are two or three drinks below normal. This simple statement will not be at all startling to the ballad-lover. He is only too well aware that without the immediate aid of alcoholic stimulant our landsmen cannot be induced to loose their tongues in song. A lethargic and inhibited crew, my merry fellows. Only with such assistance are we able to get the lead out of our feet and the frogs from our throats: not until we are pleasantly whiffled are we able to break down those walls of puritanic repression that seem to be our only birthright. Now that we are deprived of our tipple it is highly probable we will lapse into a dolorous and lugubrious silence unbroken save by a highly moralistic interference.

There was a period not so long gone, a time contemptuously called Victorian but which is now receiving the favourable attention of our most advanced historians, when we rose to the heights. It was our nearest approach to urbanity, a time when we sang and drank and danced, though we did all three quite badly. Given an even break we might have sloughed off our amateurishness and become a truly festive nation. Like all drinkers we were good fellows when we had it. . . .

Can you recall those days? The Naughty Nineties? The days when the words "naughty" and "wicked" were still uncorrupted; when a professed preference for the company of widows marked you a man of the world, a gay man-about-town? When the places that dispensed liquid refreshment had swinging doors and were called saloons: when the very best cost but fifteen cents; when a bender was called a bun; when a man who was frequently intoxicated was an old toper and not a souse? Those were the days! The never-to-be-forgotten Nineties, the dear, dead days that are gone forever.

Those were the days! Our first impulse when pleasantly jingled was to burst into mellifluous song. It required but a few similarly stimulated males to make a party. In those dear days girls were parlor fixtures and did not intrude upon the provinces of men. Far be it from the purpose of this indifferent commentator to deplore today's customs: in many ways we have a better time for their presence, a much better time indeed.

Let's get back to our party at the bar. The impulse to sing came quite early in the proceedings. Joe, he of the nervous fingers, would suggest the party retire to the back room and see if the piano was working. It was a very obvious stall: each of you knew why you went towards the piano but you continued to talk of other matters. You talked largely of Congress and the situation in Cuba, you were outspoken in your condemnation of Spain and you strongly advised American interference. More homely matters such as Irish Maggie's new baby and how the least Tim could do was to marry the girl; it was what was expected of a gentleman. Perhaps Joe didn't care much for the opinions being aired and hummed a few bars of "There'll Be a Hot Time In the Old Town Tonight" or "After the Ball." Down deep in your innocent hearts you knew this was all preparatory to the real business at hand. Joe was at the piano. Even before the sweet singer of the old Ninth Ward got on his favorites the group essayed a close harmony number, quite likely "Way Down Yonder In the Cornfield." You probably found room for complaint; the tenor was off, the second couldn't lead or something was sour. There was nothing to do but to order another round. You sat over your drink awaiting the great moment. Then Jim, who was married, got up and said he'd have to be going along before it got too late: Bill recalled that he had promised his wife he'd get up early the next morning and mow the lawn before he went to work.

Joe and Tom, bachelors, seeing their nice little party going to the dogs resolved upon stern measures. Joe turned again to the piano and picked out "I Wish I Was Single Again" in a provoking manner to make the two married men tarry a bit longer. Didn't the single fellows have all the fun? Jim and Bill would stay for just one more round if Joe would sing "Clementine." Joe did and added "Young Charlotte" for good measure. Thus heartened Joe opened the floodgates of song. He added, with the usual concomitant of beverage, "The High Barbaree" and "There is a Tavern in the Town." "Abdullah Bul-Bul Amir" was a long song and could only be appreciated by an encore round. They tried, collectively of course, "Frankie and Johnnie" and "Christofo Columbo," punctuated by more libations and met "Casey Jones" like an old friend. "The Cowboy's Lament" and "Lydia Pinkham" came, spent a few minutes, and were toasted out of the party. On and on they went through their repertory truly happy and almost free. They could not know that within a few short years their whiskey tenors and booze baritones were to be stilled forever.

The evening wore on. New members attached themselves to the party and some dropped out. Just about the time they were resinging some numbers the barkeep came in and apologetically asked the boys to have one on the house, a night cap, the place was closing and he was only obeying the law. Funny thing, in those wet and depraved days we had an inordinate respect for the law that today is quite lacking. A hurried round to polish off the night, a little close harmony on "I've Been Working On the Railroad" and out into the stilly night. Perhaps we were a little wobbly on our feet; the cop on the beat winked an eye and turned his head the other way. A good night's sleep, a bath in the morning and we were none the worse for our festal night.

The songs in this little volume are in a manner snatched from that era and those jongleurs. The music-lover who frequents the symphony concerts and delves deep into the works of Wagner and Debussy will dismiss them as trivial. He will point, if you persist, to their clichés, to their assonances and to their lack of true melody. If you attempt to sing them he will cover his ears with his hands and appeal to some ceiling deity to protect him from their dissonances. The folk-lorist will dismiss them with the phrases profane and vulgar. To him they are but the product of low resorts, gutter songs, the communal musical expression of an artistically destitute society.

My title needs a word of explanation. Away back in the good old days of long ago I found myself eagerly seeking a homestead in what was happily called "the last great West." At Tête Jaune Cache there was a straw boss known locally as "Blackie." The cockneys referred to him as "a bit of a breed" and perhaps he was. Maybe he had a bit of black or red blood mixed in with the white. He commanded our respect in a very unbreedlike way and held it as such is held out where men were supposed to be men. Blackie would get rousingly drunk, not at the Pass but in Edmonton, hammer on the bar and demand further drinks for his pious friends and drunken companions, one of which, happily at those times, I happened to be.

In using Blackie's kriegspiel I have rendered tribute where it is due and I have successfully included the two vastly different audiences for drinking songs: the singing hydropot and the warbling guzzler.

The former puts a great deal more feeling into songs glorifying inebriation than the authors ever hoped for, and the latter sings those songs in which there is little or no mention of drink or drinking. The white-ribbon lads lift their thin voices trying hard to animate the words of Ben Jonson's "Drink To Me Only With Thine Eyes" fully convinced they are singing a devilish, ribald song straight from hell's gaudy gin-mills. Any half-hearted soak could tell them it is no more a drinking song than Stevenson's "Sixteen Men on a Dead Man's Chest" is a pirate's song.

The so-called drinking songs, the songs that glorify the drinking of spiritous and fermented liquors, are weak and vapid things at their best. Almost without exception they carry the smell of the oil-lighted library lamp and show the literary striving for rhyme and effect. Only on occasion do they rise to such glory as: "The rolling English drunkard made the rolling English road" and only Chesterton could achieve that. The modern minne-singers, Belloc, Masefield and Maynard sing, for the most part, of beer and skittles and sometimes they attempt to celebrate the virtues of the lowly cider. The honest and simple reveler much prefers the sentimental and melancholy ballads.

These then are the songs professional drinkers sing when in a convivial mood. They are presented in all their tawdry garments, unprettified save that in some cases their faces and hands have been washed so they may properly appear in company. Their assonances, defective rhythms, their atrocious rhetoric, their vulgarities have been retained. As far as possible they go to you as they were sung in their prime with the hope that in your enforced aridity they may still give some pleasure.

Some were first heard in the haunts of Blackie; others came from a little Spanish bosun on a Standard Oil tankship and some from two members of the crew of the same ship, some from the sea-coast gin-mills frequented by sailors, some from the army camps in this country and France. Not a few were first heard in Luke O'Connor's Working Girl's Home, where Masefield found honorable employment serving the suds to old Ninth Warders, others in The Golden Swan, known to the literate and *cognoscenti* as The Hell Hole, still others came from homes, studios and clubs. Wherever it has been possible I have given the singer credit on the page with the ballad: a tricky memory may have slighted many, I can only ask their indulgence and acknowledge their help and interest in this manner.

Readers, meet my pious friends and drunken companions: I think you ought to know and like each other.

FRANK SHAY

Provincetown, Mass.
May 1, 1927

Acknowledgments

It is more with pleasure and honor than from any sense of duty that I acknowledge the expert and valuable assistance given me in compiling this work by Miss Helen Ramsey and Mr. Robert A. Slavin. Mine alone was the pleasurable task to listen and decide the contents: theirs to set down the words and shoehorn them into the melodies. Thanks, too, are due to Miss Packey Leveson and Miss Judith Tobey, to Messrs. James E. Harris, Adolf Bergman, William H. Wells, Cardwell Thompson, John Held, Jr., George Cronyn, Clinton Jonas, H. Douglas Hadden, Charles Somerville, and others who must remain anonymous.

"The Cowboy's Lament" is used by courtesy of John A. Lomax and the Macmillan Company.

Mr. Held's felicitous woodcuts are used through the courtesy of *The New Yorker* and editors of *Vanity Fair* and the Weyhe Gallery.

F. S.

 **THE FALLEN MAN AGAIN CAN SOAR**

BUT WOMAN FALLS TO RISE NO MORE

My Pious Friends and
Drunken Companions

"CASEY HE DANCED WITH A STRAWBERRY BLONDE.
AND THE BAND PLAYED ON"
AMERICAN FOLK SONG
—ENG BY JOHN HELD JR—

DO NOT SPIT
ON THE FLOOR

Abdullah Bul-Bul Amir*

Oh the sons of the pro-phet were val-iant and
brave And quite un-ac-customed to fear, But the
brav-est by far in the ranks of the
shah, was Ab-dul-lah Bul-Bul A-mir.

When they needed a man to encourage the van
 Or harass the foe from the rear,
Or storm a redoubt, they had only to shout
 For Abdullah Bul-Bul Amir.

There are men of renown and well known to fame
 In the army that's led by the czar,
But the best known of all was a man by the name
 Of Ivan Petrovsky Skivar.

*Sometimes known as Abdul A-Bul-Bul Amir.

He could imitate Irving, play poker and pool,
  And strum on the Spanish guitar;
In fact quite the cream of the Muscovite team,
  Was Ivan Petrovsky Skivar.

One day this bold Russian he shouldered his gun
  And with his most truculent sneer,
Was looking for fun when he happened to run
  Upon Abdullah Bul-Bul Amir.

"Young man," said Bul-Bul, "is existence so dull
  That you're anxious to end your career?
For infidel know you have trod on the toe
  Of Abdullah Bul-Bul Amir."

Said Ivan, "My friend, your remarks in the end
  Will avail you but little, I fear,
For you never will survive to repeat them alive,
  Mr. Abdullah Bul-Bul Amir."

"O, take one last look at this cool shady nook,
  And send your regrets to the czar.
By which I imply you are going to die,
  Mr. Ivan Petrovsky Skivar."

Then this haughty Mameluke drew his trusty skibouk,
  And shouting "Allah Akbar,"
And on murder bent he ferociously went
  For Ivan Petrovsky Skivar.

As Abdullah's long knife was extracting the life,
  In fact, as he shouted "Huzzah,"
He felt himself struck by that wily Kalmuck,
  Count Ivan Petrovsky Skivar.

The Sultan rode up the disturbance to quell,
  Expecting the victor to cheer,
But he only drew nigh to hear the last sigh,
  Of Abdullah Bul-Bul Amir.

Czar Petrovich too, in his uniform blue,
  Rode up in his new crested car,
He arrived just in time to exchange a last line
  With Ivan Petrovsky Skivar.

On a stone by the banks where the Danube doth roll,
  Engraved in characters clear,
Is "Stranger, remember to pray for the soul,
  Of Abdullah Bul-Bul Amir."

A Muscovite maid her long vigil doth keep,
  Alone 'neath the cold northern star,
And the name that she murmurs in vain as she weeps,
  Is Ivan Petrovsky Skivar.

The Band Played On

1. Matt Casey formed a social club that beat the town for style,
   And hired for a meeting place a hall;
   When pay day came around each week they greased the floor with
   wax,
   And danced with noise and vigor at the ball.
   Each Saturday you'd see them dressed up in Sunday clothes,
   Each lad would have his sweetheart by his side.
   When Casey led the first grand march they all would fall in line,
   Behind the man who was their joy and pride.
   For—

Chorus :

Casey would waltz with a strawberry blonde,
   And the band played on,
He'd glide 'cross the floor with the girl he ador'd.
   And the band played on,
But his brain was so loaded it nearly exploded,
The poor girl would shake with alarm.
He'd never leave the girl with the strawberry curl,
   And the band played on.

2. Such kissing in the corner and such whispering in the hall,
   And telling tales of love behind the stairs—
   As Casey was the favorite and he that ran the ball,
   Of kissing and love-making did his share.
   At twelve o'clock exactly they all would fall in line,
   Then march down to the dining-hall and eat.
   But Casey would not join them although every thing was fine,
   But he stayed upstairs and exercised his feet.
   For—

Chorus

3. Now when the dance was over and the band played "Home Sweet
   Home,"
   They played a tune at Casey's own request.
   He thanked them very kindly for the favors they had shown,
   Then he'd waltz once with the girl he loved best.
   Most all the friends are married that Casey used to know,
   And Casey too has taken him a wife.
   The blonde he used to waltz and glide with on the ballroom floor,
   Is happy Missis Casey now for life.
   For—

Chorus

O! Susanna

I came from Alabama
  Wid my banjo on my knee;
I'm gwine to Louisiana,
  My true love for to see.
It rained all night the day I left,
  The weather it was dry,
The sun so hot I froze to death;
  Susanna, don't you cry.

Chorus :

O! Susanna, O don't you cry for me;
  I've come from Alabama
Wid my banjo on my knee.

I jumped aboard de telegraph
  And trabbled down the ribber,
De 'lectric fluid magnified
  And killed five hundred nigger;
De bullgine bust, de horse run off,
  I really thought I'd die;
I shut my eyes, to hold my breath;
  Susanna, don't you cry.

Chorus

I had a dream de odder night
  When ebery t'ing was still;
I thought I saw Susanna
  A-coming down the hill;
The buckwheat cake was in her mouth,
  The tear was in her eye;
Says I, "I'm coming from the South,
  Susanna, don't you cry."

Chorus

I soon will be in New Orleans,
   And den I'll look all round,
And when I find Susanna
   I will fall upon the ground;
And if I do not find her
   Dis darkie'll surely die,
And when I'm dead and buried,
   Susanna, don't you cry.

      Chorus

Sam Bass

Sam Bass was born in Indiana, it was his native home,
   And at the age of seventeen young Sam began to roam.
Sam first came out to Texas a cowboy for to be;
   A kinder-hearted fellow you seldom ever see.

Now Sam left the Collins ranch in the merry month of May,
   With a herd of Texas cattle the Black Hills for to see.
Sold out in Custer City, went on an awful spree;
   A tougher lot of cowboys the country never see.

In coming back from Denver they robbed the U. P. train,
   They then split up in parties and started out again.
Joe Collins and his partners were overtaken soon,
   And with all their hard-earned money they had to meet their doom.

Sam made it back to Texas, all right side up with care,
   Rode into the town of Denton with all his friends to share.
But his career was short in Texas, three robberies did he do,
   He held up all the passengers, the mail and express cars, too.

Sam had four companions, four brave and daring lads:
   They were Richardson, Jackson, Joe Collins and Old Dad;
Four more bold and daring cowboys the ranchers never knew,
   They whipped the Texas Rangers and ran the boys in blue.

Sam had another companion, called Arkansaw for short,
  He was shot by a Texas Ranger by the name of Thomas Fort.
O, Tom was a big six-footer and thought him mighty fly,
  But I can tell you his racket, he was a deadbeat on the sly.

Jim Murphy borrowed Sam's good gold and then refused to pay,
  The only shot he fired was to give poor Sam away.
Jim sold out Sam and Barnes and left their friends to mourn,
  But what a scorching Jim will get when Gabriel blows his horn.

Sam Bass met his fate at Round Rock, July the twenty-first,
  They filled poor Sam with rifle balls and emptied out his purse,
And now he is a corpse and his body turned to clay,
  And Jackson's gone to Mexico and there I guess he'll stay.

Brother Noah

Broth-er No-ah Broth-er No-ah May
I come in-to the Ark of the Lord for it's
grow-ing ve-ry dark and it's rain-ing ve-ry hard Hal-le
loo Hal-le loo Hal-le loo-oo-oo-oo-ia.

2. No, you can't sir, no, you can't, sir,
   You can't come into the ark of the Lord
   Though it's growing very dark and it's raining very hard.
   Halleloo, halleloo, halleloo, hallelujah!

3. Very well, sir, very well, sir,
   You can go to the dickens with your darned old scow,
   'Cause it ain't goin' to rain very hard no how.
   Halleloo, halleloo, halleloo, hallelujah!

4. That's a lie, sir, that's a lie, sir,
   You can darn soon tell that it ain't no sell,
   'Cause it's sprinklin' now and it's goin' to rain like hell.
   Halleloo, halleloo, halleloo, hallelujah!

The Butcher's Boy

In Jer-sey City, where I did dwell, A butcher's boy I loved so well; He court-ed me my heart a-way, And now with me he will not stay.

2. There is a house in this same town,
   Where my true love goes and sits him down;
   He takes a strange girl on his knee,
   And tells her what he won't tell me.

3. 'Tis grief for me, I'll tell you why,
   Because she has more gold than I;
   Her gold will melt and silver fly,
   She'll see the day she's poor as I.

4. I went upstairs to make my bed,
   And nothing to my mother said,
   I took a chair and sit me down,
   With pen and ink I wrote it down.

*Some versions have it "Dublin City": Boston City, in fact, New York City, will serve equally well. Obviously it is the natural brother of "There Is a Tavern In The Town."

5. On every line I dropped a tear,
   While calling home my Willie dear. . . .
   Her father he came home that night,
   "Where, Oh where has my darling gone?"

6. He went upstairs, the door he broke,
   And found her hanging by a rope.
   He took his knife and cut her down,
   And on her breast these lines he found:

7. "Go dig my grave both wide and deep,
   Place a marble stone at my head and feet.
   Upon my breast a marble dove
   To show them that I died for love."

Casey Jones*

Come all you rounders if you want to hear,
A story about a brave engineer,
Casey Jones was the rounder's name,
On a six-eight wheeler, boys, he won his fame.
The caller called Casey at half past four,
Kissed his wife at the station door,
Mounted to the cabin with his orders in his hand,
And took his farewell trip to that promised land.

   Casey Jones! Mounted to the cabin,
   Casey Jones with his orders in his hand.
   Casey Jones! Mounted to his cabin,
   And took his farewell trip to that promised land.

Put in your water and shovel in your coal,
Put your head out the window, watch them drivers roll,
I'll run her till she leaves the rail,
'Cause I'm eight hours late with that western mail.

*Literally K. C. Jones; Kansas City Jones.

He looked at his watch, and his watch was slow,
He looked at his water and the water was low,
He turned to the fireman and he said,
"We're going to reach Frisco but we'll all be dead."

   Casey Jones! Going to reach Frisco,
   Casey Jones! But we'll all be dead.
   Casey Jones! Going to reach Frisco,
   We're going to reach Frisco, but we'll all be dead.

Casey pulled up that Reno hill,
He tooted for the crossing with an awful shrill,
The switchman knew by the engine's moans
That the man at the throttle was Casey Jones.
He pulled up within two miles of the place,
Number Four stared him right in the face,
Turned to the fireman, said, "Boy, you'd better jump,
'Cause there's two locomotives that's a-going to bump."

   Casey Jones! Two locomotives!
   Casey Jones! That's a-going to bump!
   Casey Jones! Two locomotives!
   There's two locomotives that's a-going to bump.

Casey said just before he died,
"There's two more roads that I'd like to ride."
Fireman said, "What could they be?"
"The Southern Pacific and the Santa Fe."
Mrs. Jones sat on her bed a-sighing,
Just received a message that Casey was dying,
Said, "Go to bed, children, and hush your crying,
'Cause you got another papa on the Salt Lake Line."

   Casey Jones! Got another papa!
   Casey Jones! On that Salt Lake Line!
   Casey Jones! Got another papa!
   And you've got another papa on that Salt Lake Line.

Casey Jones II

A more artless variant was heard on a Canadian Northern work train out where, as the travel brochures have it, the "last great West begins":

Come all you rounders for I want you to hear
The story told of a brave engineer;
Casey Jones was the rounder's name
On a heavy six-eight wheeler he rode to fame.

Caller called Jones about half past four,
Jones kissed his wife at the station door,
Climbed into the cab with the orders in his hand,
Says, "This is my trip to the promised land."

Through South Memphis yards on the fly,
He heard the firemen say, "You've got a white-eye."
All the switchmen knew by the engine's moans,
That the hogger at the throttle was Casey Jones.

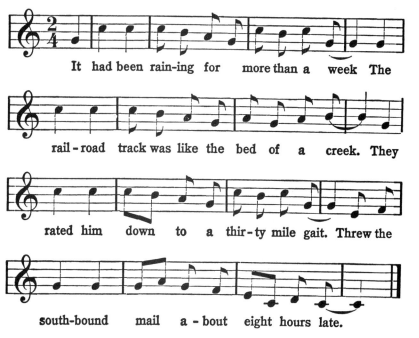

It had been rain-ing for more than a week The
rail-road track was like the bed of a creek. They
rated him down to a thir-ty mile gait. Threw the
south-bound mail a-bout eight hours late.

*Music Copyright 1909. Copyright Renewed 1936 and Assigned to Shapiro, Bernstein & Co., Inc., New York. Used by permission.

Fireman says, "Casey, you're runnin' too fast,
You run the block signal the last station you passed."
Jones says, "Yes, I think we can make it, though,
For she steams much better than ever I know."

Jones says, "Fireman, don't you fret,
Keep knockin' at the firedoor, don't give up yet;
I'm goin' to run her till she leaves the rail
Or make it on time with the south-bound mail."

Around the curve and a-down the dump,
Two locomotives were a-bound to bump,
Fireman hollered, "Jones, it's just ahead,
We might jump and make it but we'll all be dead."

'Twas around this curve he saw a passenger train,
Something happened in Casey's brain;
Fireman jumped off, but Jones stayed on,
He's a good engineer but he's dead and gone.

Poor Casey Jones was always all right,
He stuck to his post both day and night:
They loved to hear the whistle of old Number Three
As he came into Memphis on the old K. C.

Headaches and heartaches and all kinds of pain
Are not apart from a railroad train;
Tales that are earnest, noble and gran'
Belong to the life of a railroad man.

Navy Fragment

Oh, the captain went below,
For to light the cabin lamp;
But he couldn't light the lamp
Because the wick was too dam' damp.
Heave-ho, you sons of glory,
    The Golden Gates are passed.

Forty-nine Bottles

Forty-nine bottles hanging on the wall.
Forty-nine bottles hanging on the wall.
Take one away from them all,
Forty-eight bottles hanging on the wall.

Continue ad lib, ad nauseam.

Ach, Du Lieber Augustine

Ach du lieber Augustine, Augustine, Augustine,
Ach du lieber Augustine alles ist hin!
Geld ist weg, Mädl ist weg, alles weg, alles weg,
Ach du lieber Augustine alles ist hin!

I Wanta Go Home

I wanta go home, I wanta go home,
The bullets they whistle, the cannons they roar.
I don't wanta go to the trenches no more.
Ship me over the sea,
Where the Allemand can't get at me:
O, my! I'm too young to die,
I wanta go home!

In the Sweet Bye and Bye

Long haired preachers come out every night,
   Try to tell you what's wrong and what's right;
But when asked about something to eat,
   They will answer in accents so sweet:

      You will eat bye and bye,
      In the glorious land of the sky.
         Work and pray,
         Live on hay,
      You'll have pie in the sky when you die!

Christofo Columbo

In four-teen hun-dred and nine - ty - two, down

in a Span-ish al - ley, A wop was run-ning

up and down shout-ing "Hot ta - ma - le." Oh

Christ - o - fo Col - um - bo, He thought the world was

round - o, That pi - o - neer - ing Buc - ca -

neer - ing Son-of - a - gun Col - um - bo.

2. Columbus came from Italee,
     He was full of pink confetti
  He showed the Queen of Spain,
     How to manage her spaghetti.

          Oh, Christofo Columbo,
          Knew land it could be found-o,
          That heathen-hating, navigating,
          Son-of-a-gun, Columbo!

3. He rushed up to the Queen one day,
     Said, "Give me ships and cargo,
  I'll be a sea-going, son-of-a-gun
     If I don't bring back Chicago."

          Oh, Christofo Columbo,
          He thought the world was round-o,
          That encroaching, queen-approaching,
          Son-of-a-gun, Columbo!

4. The Queen she said to Ferdinand,
     "His scheme sounds like a daisy."
  "To hell with him," said Ferdinand,
     "I think the wop is crazy."

          Oh, Christofo Columbo,
          He thought the world was round-o,
          That pioneering, buccaneering,
          Son-of-a-gun, Columbo!

5. "It isn't ships or men he wants,
     For something else he's shootin',
  And if he hangs around you much,
     He'll lose his head right tootin'.

          Oh, Christofo Columbo,
          Knew that gold could be found-o,
          That brave seafaring, never-caring,
          Son-of-a-gun, Columbo!

6. Said Columbo, "Now, Isabelle,
     Don't act so gosh darned funny,
   I need the ships and the men
     So pony up the money."

       Oh, Christofo Columbo,
       He knew ships could be found-o,
       That always busted, never trusted,
       Son-of-a-gun, Columbo!

7. Said Isabelle, "Now wait awhile,
     And cut out this flam-flimmin';
   You've only asked for ships and men
     But how about some wimmin?"

       Oh, Christofo Columbo,
       He knew the world was round-o,
       This goll-durning, woman spurning
       Son-of-a-gun, Columbo!

8. On the day they sailed away,
     The people thought them crazy.
   Columbus said, "No janes on board,
     The sailors won't get lazy."

       Oh, Christofo Columbo,
       Never could be bound-o,
       That woman-hating, captivating
       Son-of-a-gun, Columbo!

9. In fourteen hundred and ninety-two,
     Across the broad Atlantic;
   The sailors all were filled with grief,
     Their wives were nearly frantic.

       Oh, Christofo Columbo,
       He knew the world was round-o,
       That family-breaking, history-making,
       Son-of-a-gun, Columbo!

10. In fourteen hundred and ninety-two,
     The doctors were not many,
   The only one they had on board
     Was a gosh-darned quack named Benny.

        Oh, Christofo Columbo,
        He knew the world was round-o,
        That philosophic, philanthropic,
        Son-of-a-gun, Columbo!

11. Colombo's ears ached him one day,
     But Benny was quite placid.
   He filled up both Columbo's ears,
     With hot mercuric acid.

        Oh, Christofo Columbo,
        Knew doctors could be drowned-o,
        That democratic and autocratic,
        Son-of-a-gun, Columbo!

12. They anchored near San Salvydor,
     In search of women and booty;
   A pretty girl stood on the shore,
     Columbo said, "Do your duty."

        Oh, Christofo Columbo,
        Found here was solid ground-o,
        That stop-your-shoving, woman-loving,
        Son-of-a-gun, Columbo!

13. The sailors jumped into the surf,
     And shed their coats and collars,
   Columbo said, "The first one there
     Will get a hundred dollars."

        Oh, Christofo Columbo,
        Knew where he was bound-o,
        That woman-baiting, captivating,
        Son-of-a-gun, Columbo!

14. He settled down to stay awhile,
      But things were not so pretty,
    The sailors started getting drunk
      Which really was a pity.

          Oh, Christofo Columbo,
          Got to where he was bound-o,
          That heavy-headed, always-dreaded,
          Son-of-a-gun, Columbo!

15. One day they loaded him in chain,
      And shipped him back to Spain.
    Columbo said, "I'm done for good
      These doings give me a pain."

          Oh, Christofo Columbo,
          He proved the world was round-o,
          That pioneering, persevering,
          Son-of-a-gun, Columbo!

16. When Columbo got back to Sunny Spain,
      He told them of bonanzas,
    They answered him, "We notice, Wop,
      You ain't got no bananas."

          Oh, Christofo Columbo,
          He showed the world was round-o,
          That poorly treated, badly cheated,
          Son-of-a-gun, Columbo!

Clementine

As sung by Ralph Geddes

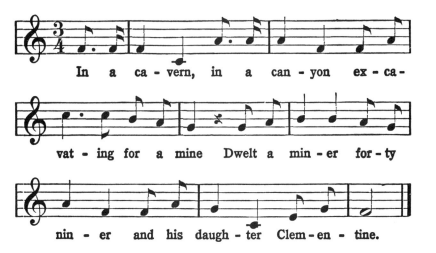

In a ca - vern, in a can - yon ex - ca - vat - ing for a mine Dwelt a min - er for - ty nin - er and his daugh - ter Clem - en - tine.

Chorus :

Oh, my darling, oh my darling, oh my darling Clementine !
Thou art lost and gone for ever, dreadful sorry, Clementine.

Light she was, and like a feather,
And her shoes were number nine,
Sardine-boxes, without topses,
Sandals were for Clementine.

Chorus

Drove she ducklings to the water,
Every morning just at nine,
Stubbed her toe upon a splinter,
Fell into the foaming brine.

Chorus

Ruby lips above the water,
Blowing bubbles soft and fine,
Alas, for me! I was no swimmer,
So I lost my Clementine.

Chorus

In a churchyard, near the canyon,
Where the myrtle doth entwine,
There grow roses, and other posies,
Fertilized by Clementine.

Chorus

Then the miner, forty-niner,
Soon began to peak and pine,
Thought he 'oughter jine' his daughter,
Now he's with his Clementine.

Chorus

In my dreams she oft doth haunt me,
With her garments soaked in brine,
Though in life I used to hug her,
Now she's dead I draw the line.

Chorus

When I Die

When I die, don't bury me at all,
Just pickle my bones in alcohol:
A scuttle of booze
At my head and shoes,
   And then my bones will surely keep.

One More Drink for the Four of Us

I was drunk last night,
  Drunk the night before;
Going to get drunk tonight
  If I never get drunk any more.

    'Cause when I'm drunk
      I'm as happy as can be:
    For I am a member
      Of the souse familee.

Glorious, glorious,
  One more drink for the four of us.
Sing glory be to hob there's no more of us
  For one of us could kill it all alone.

Sweet Rosie

Sweet Rosie Levinsky,
She was a blacksmith by birth.
She was tired of living
And decided to leave this old earth.
She tried dying by inches,
But finding that this was too hard,
She went out in the alley
Laid down and died by the yard. . . .

                    (spoken) three feet.

The Foggy, Foggy Dew

For I am a weaver and I live all alone,
And I work at the weavers' trade,
And the only, only thing I ever did wrong
Was to woo a fair young maid.
I wooed her in the summer time, part of the winter, too,
And there were many, many times
That I held her in my arms,
Just to keep her from the foggy, foggy dew.

One night she came to my bedside
When I was fast asleep.
Oh, that pretty little maid came to my bedside
And there began to weep.
She wept, she cried, she damn near died,
Alas, what could I do? So come cuddle into bed
To that pretty maid I said,
And I'll keep you from the foggy, foggy dew.

Now I am a bachelor and I live with my son
And we work at the weavers' trade.
And every time that I look into his eyes,
He reminds me of that fair young maid.
They remind me of the summer time,
Part of the winter, too;
Of the many, many times I held her in my arms,
Just to keep her from the foggy, foggy dew.

A Catch

A hoss and a flea an' a little mice,
Settin' in the corner shootin' dice;
Hoss foot slipped and he sot on the flea,
Flea sang out, "That's a hoss on me."

The Ballad Of Captain Kidd

My name was William* Kidd, when I sailed, when I sailed,
　　My name was William Kidd, when I sailed,
　　　　My name was William Kidd,
　　　　God's laws I did forbid,
And so wickedly I did, when I sailed.

My parents taught me well, when I sailed, when I sailed,
　　My parents taught me well, when I sailed,
　　　　My parents taught me well,
　　　　To shun the gates of hell,
But against them I rebelled, when I sailed.

I'd a Bible in my hand, when I sailed, when I sailed,
　　I'd a Bible in my hand, when I sailed,
　　　　I'd a Bible in my hand,
　　　　By my father's great command,
And I sunk it in the sand, when I sailed.

I murdered William Moore, as I sailed, as I sailed,
　　I murdered William Moore, as I sailed
　　　　I murdered William Moore,
　　　　And laid him in his gore,
Not many leagues from shore, as I sailed.

I was sick and nigh to death, when I sailed, when I sailed,
　　I was sick and nigh to death, when I sailed,
　　　　I was sick and nigh to death,
　　　　And I vowed with every breath,
To walk in wisdom's ways, when I sailed.

*Kidd's name was given as Robert in the original version.

I thought I was undone, as I sailed, as I sailed,
   I thought I was undone, as I sailed,
      I thought I was undone,
      And my wicked glass had run,
But health did soon return, as I sailed.

My repentance lasted not, as I sailed, as I sailed,
   My repentance lasted not, as I sailed,
      My repentance lasted not,
      My vows I soon forgot,
Damnation was my lot, as I sailed.

I spied the ships from France, as I sailed, as I sailed,
   I spied the ships of France, as I sailed,
      I spied the ships of France,
      To them I did advance,
And took them all by chance, as I sailed.

I spied the ships of Spain, as I sailed, as I sailed,
   I spied the ships of Spain, as I sailed,
      I spied the ships of Spain,
      I looted them for gain,
'Till most of them was slain, as I sailed.

I'd ninety bars of gold, as I sailed, as I sailed,
   I'd ninety bars of gold, as I sailed,
      I'd ninety bars of gold,
      And dollars manifold,
With riches uncontrolled, as I sailed.

Thus being o'er-taken at last, as I sailed, as I sailed,
   Thus being o'er-taken at last, as I sailed,
      Thus being o'er-taken at last,
      And into prison cast,
And sentence being passed, I must die.

Farewell, the raging main, I must die, I must die,
    Farewell, the raging main, I must die,
        Farewell, the raging main,
          To Turkey, France and Spain,
I shall never see you again, for I must die.

To Execution Dock, I must go, I must go,
    To Execution Dock, I must go,
        To Execution Dock,
          While many thousands flock,
But I must bear the shock, and must die.

Come all ye young and old, see me die, see me die,
    Come all ye young and old, see me die,
        Come all ye young and old,
          You're welcome to my gold,
For by it I've lost my soul, and must die.

Take warning now by me, for I must die, for I must die,
    Take warning now by me, for I must die,
        Take warning now by me,
          And shun bad company,
Lest you come to hell with me, for I die.

The Old Grey Mare

The old grey mare ain't what she used to be,
    Ain't what she used to be;
    Ain't what she used to be;
O, the old grey mare ain't what she used to be
    Twenty years ago.
Twenty years ago, twenty years ago!
O, the old grey mare ain't what she used to be
    Twenty years ago.

The Dying Hobo

As sung by Helen Ramsey

Beside a western water tank,
  One cold November day;
Sheltered by a box car
  The dying hobo lay.

His partner sat beside him
  And slowly stroked his head;
As he listened to the last words
  The dying hobo said.

"I'm going to a better land,
  Where everything is bright;
Where handouts grow on bushes
  And you sleep out every night."

"Where a man don't ever have to work,
  Or even change his socks;
And little streams of whiskey
  Come trickling down the rocks."

"Just tell my girl in Denver,
  Her face no more I'll view,
For I'm going to hop a fast freight
  And ride her right straight through."

His eyes grew dim, his head fell back,
  He'd sung his last refrain.
His partner hooked his coat and pants,
  And caught an eastbound train.

Way Down Yonder in the Cornfield

Some folks say that a nigger won't steal,
  'Way down, 'way down, 'way down yonder in the cornfield.
But I caught a couple in my cornfield,
  'Way down, 'way down, 'way down yonder in the cornfield.

.   .   .   .   .

Forty miles from whiskey
And sixty miles from gin.

I'm leaving this damned country
For to live a life of sin.

The Lamentable History of Frankie and Johnnie

As sung by altogether too many persons

There are countless verses to this indubitably American folk-song and most of them are, quite honestly, ribald and unprintable. I have no sympathy for those commentators who insist that it is the unnatural spawn of the Negro melody, "Frankie and Albert." Surely the infidelity of the lover does not make it Negroid. My conclusions are that the latter is an Afro-American variant of the genuine ballad which found great favor among the covered wagon pioneers and Civil War soldiers.

The verses given herewith for all their limitations tell the story. They will serve as a starting point for those who know but a few scattered verses and as a basis for controversy for Frankie and Johnnie fans.

Arrangement by Clinton Jonas.

Frank - ie and John - ie were lov - ers.

O my gawd how they could love, they

swore to be true to each oth - er, Just as

true as the stars up a - bove, He was her

man.... but he done her wrong....

2. Frankie she was a good woman,
   And Johnnie he was her man.
   And every dollar Frankie made
   Went right into Johnnie's hand.
   He was her man, but he done her wrong!

3. Frankie she was a good woman,
   Just like everyone knows,
   She paid a hundred dollars
   For every suit of Johnnie's clothes.
   He was her man, but he done her wrong!

4. Frankie and Johnnie went walking,
   Johnnie in his brand new suit.
   "O, my gawd," said Frankie,
   "But doesn't Johnnie look cute?"
   He was her man, but he done her wrong!

5. Frankie went down to Memphis,
   She went on the morning train,
   She paid a hundred dollars,
   For Johnnie a watch and chain.
   He was her man, but he done her wrong!

6. Frankie lived down at the crib-house★
   Crib-house with only two doors,
   Gave all her money to Johnnie,
   He spent it on those call-house girls.
   He was her man, but he done her wrong!

7. Frankie and Johnnie, those lovers,
   They had a quarrel one day,
   Johnnie he up and told Frankie,
   "Bye-bye, Babe, I'm goin' away,
   I was your man, but I'm just gone!"

8. Frankie went down to the gin-mill,
   To get herself a glass of beer,
   She said to that great big bartender,
   "Have you seen my lovin' man around here?
   'Cause he is my man and he wouldn't do me wrong."

9. "Ain't goin' to tell you no stories,
   Ain't goin' to tell you no lie,
   I saw your man 'bout an hour ago
   With a hussy named Ella Fly:
   And if he is your man, he's doin' you wrong."

★Crib-house: bed-house or lodging-house.

10. Frankie went down to the hockshop,
    She didn't go there for fun.
  She pawned all her jewelry
    And bought a great big forty-four gun,
      For to kill that man who was doing her wrong!

11. Frankie went down to the call-house,
    She leaned on that call-house bell,
  "Get out of the way all chippies and fools
    Or I'll blow you straight to hell;
      I want my man who is doing me wrong."

12. Frankie looked over the transom,
    And there to her great surprise,
  Yes, there on a couch sat Johnnie
    A-lovin' up that Ella Fly.
      He was her man and he was doing her wrong!

13. The girls all said to Frankie,
    "Frankie, now don't you shoot."
  But Frankie pulled down on the trigger
    And the gun went roota-toot-toot,
      Into that man who had done her wrong!

14. First time she shot him he staggered,
    Second time she shot him he fell,
  Third time she shot him, O Lordy,
    There was a new man's face in hell.
      She'd killed that man, who had done her wrong!

15. "O, roll me over, sweetheart,
    O, roll me over slow,
  O, roll me over on my right side
    Where the bullets ain't hurtin' me so.
      I was your man but I done you wrong."

16. After she shot him she was sorry,
    And it wrang her poor heart sore,

To see her loving Johnnie
  Stretched across that hotel floor.
    But he was her man and he done her wrong!

17. Frankie went down to the undertaker's,
      And ordered up a casket sound;
    All lined with silks and satins—
      The best that could be found,
        To bury that man who had done her wrong!

18. Bring on your open barouches,
      Bring on your rubber tired hack.
    Seven goin' down to the cemetery
      But there's only six a-comin' back.
        They're planting that man who had done her wrong!

19. "O, bring 'round a thousand policemen,
      Bring 'em around today,
    To lock me in the dungeon
      And throw the key away.
        I shot my man who was doing me wrong."

20. "Yes, put me in that dungeon,
      Oh, put me in that cell,
    Put me where the north-west wind blows
      From the south-east corner of hell.
        I killed my man who had done me wrong."

21. Frankie she said to the warden,
      "What are they going to do?"
    The warden he said to Frankie,
      "It's the electric chair for you!
        You killed your man because he done you wrong."

22. The sheriff came 'round in the morning,
      He said it was all for the best;
    He said her lover Johnnie
      Was nothin' but a gawdam pest.
        He was her man and he done her wrong.

23. Frankie she sits in her crib-house,
      Underneath the electric fan,
   Telling her little sister,
      To beware of the gawdam man.
         "He'll do you wrong, just as sure as you're born."

24. This story has no moral,
      This story has no end,
   This story only goes to show
      That there ain't no good in men.
         They'll do you wrong just as sure's you're born.

Just a Wee Doch-an-Dorris

Just a wee doch-an-dorris,
Just a wee drap that's a',
Just a wee doch-an-dorris'
Before we gang awa'.
There's a wee wifie waitin'
With a wee bairn or two:
For if you can say
It's a braw brecht,
Moonlecht necht:
Yer a' recht, that's a'.

Hail, Hail!

Hail, hail, the gang's all here,
So what the hell do we care?
What the hell do we care?
Hail, hail, the gang's all here,
So what the hell do we care now?

The Dying Fisherman's Song

'Twas midnight on the ocean,
　Not a street car was in sight;
The sun was shining brightly,
　For it had rained all that night.

'Twas a summer's day in winter,
　The rain was snowing fast,
As a barefoot girl with shoes on
　Stood sitting in the grass.

'Twas evening and the rising sun
　Was setting in the west;
And all the fishes in the trees
　Were cuddled in their nests.

The rain was pouring down,
　The sun was shining bright,
And everything that you could see
　Was hidden out of sight.

The organ peeled potatoes,
　Lard was rendered by the choir;
When the sexton rang the dishrag
　Someone set the church on fire.

"Holy smokes!" the teacher shouted,
　As he madly tore his hair.
Now his head resembles heaven,
　For there is no parting there.

I Had But Fifty Cents

As sung by James E. Harris

I took my girl to a ball last night, 'twas such a fan - cy hop, We stayed un - til the folks went home, the mu - sic it did stop; Then to a rest - au - rant we went, The fin - est on the street She said she was - n't hun - gry but this is what she'd eat:

2. A dozen raw, a plate of slaw, some fancy Boston roast,
   Some turtle stew, crackers, too, some soft-shelled crab on toast;
   Next she tried some oysters fried—her appetite was immense!
   She asked for pie! I thought I'd die, for I had but fifty cents!

3. After eating all of this she smiled so very sweet;
   She said she wasn't hungry at all, she wished that she could eat.
   But the very next order that she gave, my heart within me sank:
   She said she wasn't thirsty at all, but this is what she drank:

4. A brandy, a gin, a big hot rum, a schooner of lager beer,
   Some whiskey skins and two more gins did quickly disappear;
   A bottle of ale, a soda cocktail, she astonished all the gents!
   She called for more, I fell on the floor, for I had but fifty cents.

5. To finish up, this delicate girl cleaned out an ice cream can;
   She says, "Now, Sam, I'll tell mama you're such a nice young man."
   She said she'd bring her sister along next time she came, for fun;
   I handed the man my fifty cents, and this is what he done:

6. He broke my nose, he tore my clothes, he knocked me out of breath;
   I took the prize for two black eyes, he kicked me most to death;
   At every chance he made me dance, he fired me over the fence.
   Take my advice: don't try it twice, when you have but fifty cents.

I've Been Workin' on the Railroad

I've been workin' on the railroad,
　　All the live long day:
I've been workin' on the railroad
　　Just to pass the time away.
Don't you hear the whistle tooting?
　　Rise up so early in the morn.
Don't you hear the foreman shouting?
　　Dinah, blow your horn.

Little Brown Jug

My wife and I live all alone
  In a little brown hut we call our own,
She loves gin and I love rum,
  Tell you what, don't we have fun?

  Chorus :

    Ha, ha, ha, 'Tis you and me,
    Little brown jug don't I love thee?
    Ha, ha, ha, 'Tis you and me,
    Little brown jug don't I love thee?

If I had a cow that gave such milk
  I'd dress her in the finest silk,
Feed her on the choicest hay,
  And milk her forty times a day.

  Chorus

'Tis you that makes my friends my foes,
  'Tis you that makes me wear old clothes,
But seeing you are so near my nose,
  Tip her up and down she goes.

  Chorus

When I go toiling on my farm,
  Take little brown jug under my arm,
Set it under some shady tree,
  Little brown jug, don't I love thee?

  Chorus

Then came the landlord tripping in,
 Round top hat and peaked chin,
In his hand he carried a cup,
 Says I, "Old fellow, give us a sup."

   Chorus

If all the folks of Adam's race,
 Were put together in one place,
Then I'd prepare to drop a tear
 Before I'd part with you, my dear.

   Chorus

I Know Where They Are

If you want to find the Majors
 I know where they are,
   Yes, I know where they are.
If you want to find the Majors
 I know where they are,
Down in the deep dugout,
 I saw them, I saw them,
Down in the deep dugout,
 I saw them
   Down in the deep dugout.

I'm Full

I'm full, absolutely full,
But I know the country I was born in.
My name is Jock McGraw
And I dinna care a straw,
For I've a wee bit drappie
In the bottle for the mornin'.

Jesse James

From William H. Wells, New York

How the people held their breath
When they heard of Jesse's death
   And wondered how he came to die;
For the big reward
Little Robert Ford
   Shot Jesse James on the sly.

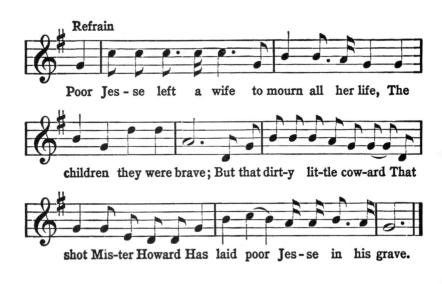

Poor Jes - se left a wife to mourn all her life, The children they were brave; But that dirt-y lit-tle cow-ard That shot Mis-ter Howard Has laid poor Jes-se in his grave.

Jesse was a man,
A friend of the poor,
   Never did he suffer a man's pain;
And with his brother Frank
He robbed the Chicago bank,
   And stopped the Glendale train.

Chorus

BUT THAT DIRTY LITTLE COWARD,
THAT SHOT MR. HOWARD,
HAS LAID POOR JESSE IN HIS GRAVE

AMERICAN FOLKSONG   ENG. BY JOHN HELD JR. WITH A HI AND A HO

HER BEAUTY SHE SOLD FOR AN OLD MANS GOLD
SHE'S A BIRD IN A GILDED CAGE

BY JOHN HELD JR   THE PIONEER   ENGRAVER

Jesse goes to rest
With his hand on his breast,
   And the devil will be upon his knees;
He was born one day
In the county of Clay,
   And came from a great race.

      Chorus

Men when you go out to the West,
   Don't be afraid to die;
With the law in their hand,
But they didn't have the sand
   For to take Jesse James alive.

      Chorus

Back and Side Go Bare, Go Bare!

This version, attributed to Bishop John Still, was a modernization of a twelfth-century ballad. It sounds as though it might find great favor at Oxford.

Back and side go bare, go bare!
   Both foot and hand grow cold;
But belly, God send thee good ale enough,
   Whether it be new or old.

I cannot eat but little meat,
   My stomach is not good;
But sure I think that I can drink
   With him that wears a hood.
Though I go bare, take ye no care,
   I nothing am a-cold.
I stuff my skin so full within
   Of jolly good ale and old.

Back and side go bare, go bare
  Both foot and hand grow cold;
But belly, God send thee good ale enough,
  Whether it be new or old.

I have no roast but a nut-brown toast,
  And a crab laid in the fire;
A little bread shall do me stead,
  Much bread I do not desire.
No frost nor snow, nor wind I trow,
  Can hurt me if I wold;
I am so wrapped, and thoroughly lapped,
  Of jolly good ale and old.

Back and side go bare, etc.

And Tib my wife, that as her life
  Loveth well good ale to seek,
Full oft drinks she, till ye may see
  The tears run down her cheek;
Then doth she trowl to me the bowl,
  Even as a maltworm should,
And saith, Sweetheart, I took my part
  Of this jolly good ale and old.

Back and side go bare, etc.

Then let them drink till they nod and wink,
  Even as good fellows should do;
They shall not miss to have the bliss
  Good ale doth bring men to:
And all poor souls that have scoured bowls,
  Or have them lustily trowled,
God save the lives of them and their wives,
  Whether they be young or old.

Back and side go bare, etc.

Fill the Flowing Bowl

Early eighteenth-century ballad.

He that drinketh strong beer and goes to bed right mellow,
Lives as he ought to live and dies a hearty fellow.

Chorus :

Come, landlord, fill the flowing bowl
Until it does run over.
For tonight we'll merry be, merry be, merry be,
Tomorrow we'll get sober.

He that drinketh small beer and goes to bed quite sober,
Falls as the leaves do fall that die in dull October.

Chorus

Punch cures the gout, the colic and the phthisic,*
And is to all men the very best of physic.

Chorus

He that courts a pretty girl, and courts her for his pleasure,
Is a knave unless he marries her without store or treasure.

Chorus

Now let us dance and sing and drive away all sorrow,
For perhaps we may not meet again tomorrow.

Chorus :

Come landlord, fill the flowing bowl
Until it does run over.
For tonight we'll merry be, merry be, merry be,
Tomorrow we'll get sober.

*Tisic, a progressive wasting disease, especially pulmonary consumption.

Le Chef de Gare

Le chef de gare
Il est coucou,
Le chef de gare
Il est coucou,
Qui est coucou ?
Le chef de gare.
C'est que sa femme
Voulut—voulut—
Oh—ee. Oh—ee
Voulut—Voulut.

The Ballad Of Lydia Pinkham

As sung by John Fitzgerald

When we sing of Lydia Pinkham
  And how she loved the human race,
And how she sold her vegetable compound,
  And how the papers published her face,
            published her face!

O, Mrs. Brown could do no housework,
  O, Mrs. Brown could do no housework,
She took three bottles of Lydia's compound,
  And now there's nothing she will shirk,
            she will shirk!

O, Mrs. Jones, etc.
O, Mrs. White, etc.
O, Mrs. Green, etc.

Another version is

Mrs. Jones she had no children,
  And she loved them very dear.
So she took six bottles of Pinkham's—
  Now she has twins every year.

Chorus :

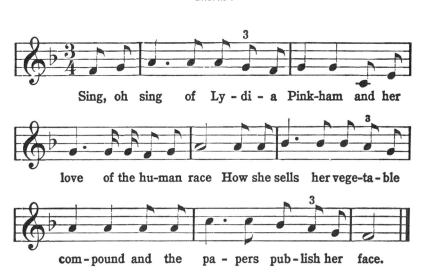

Sing, oh sing of Ly - di - a Pink-ham and her love of the hu-man race How she sells her vege-ta-ble com - pound and the pa - pers pub - lish her face.

Lottie Smyth ne'er had a lover,
  Blotchy pimples caused her plight;
But she took nine bottles of Pinkham's—
  Sweethearts swarm about her each night.

Railroad Bill

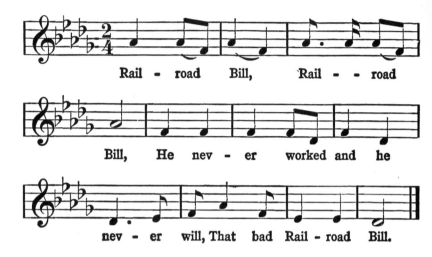

Rail - road   Bill,   Rail - - road

Bill,   He   nev - er   worked and   he

nev - er   will, That   bad   Rail - road   Bill.

Railroad Bill, mighty bad man.
Shoot all de lamps off de stan',
   That bad Railroad Bill.

Railroad Bill, so mean and so bad,
Took ev'ything the po' farmer had,
   That bad Railroad Bill.

Somebody went home an' tol' my wife,
All about—well, my pas' life,
   Wus that Railroad Bill.

Railroad Bill never had no wife,
Always lookin' for someone's life,
   That bad Railroad Bill.

I'm goin' home and tell my wife,
Railroad Bill tried to take my life,
   Yes, bad Railroad Bill.

Ol' Macmillan had a special train,
When he got there wus a shower of rain,
      Wus lookin' for Railroad Bill.

Ev'ybody tol' him he better go back,
Railroad Bill wus comin' down de track,
      Wus Railroad Bill.

Railroad Bill was the worst ol' coon,
Shot Macmillan by the light of de moon,
      Yes, that bad Railroad Bill.

Sheriff came a-knockin' at de do'
Said he was lookin' fo' me no mo',
      Lookin' for Railroad Bill.

Ten policemen all dressed in blue,
Comin' down the street two by two,
      Lookin' for Railroad Bill.

Ev'body tol' him he better go back,
Policemen comin' down de railroad track,
      An' a-lookin' for Railroad Bill.

Railroad Bill, a-waitin' at de tank,
Waitin' fo' de train called de Nancy Hank,
      In the mornin' jus' 'fo day.

Ol' Culpepper went up on Number Five,
Goin' bring him back dead or alive,
      That bad Railroad Bill.

Railroad Bill said befo' he died,
Goin' build a railroad fo' de hoboes to ride,
      Ride on, Railroad Bill.

First on de table, nex' on de wall,
Ol' corn whiskey cause of it all,
        Done lookin' fo' Railroad Bill.

Railroad Bill led a mighty bad life,
Always hookin' some other man's wife,
        That bad Railroad Bill.

The Morning After

A gilded mirror, a polished bar,
   A million glasses, straws in a jar:
A courteous young man, all dressed in white,
   Are my recollections of last night!

The streets were dirty and far too long,
   Gutters sloppy and policemen strong:
The slamming of doors in a sea-going hack;
   That's my recollection of getting back!

The stairs were narrow and hard to climb,
   I rested often for I'd lots of time:
An awkward keyhole, a misplaced chair,
   Told the folks plainly I was there!

A heated interior, a wobbly bed,
   A sea-sick man with an aching head:
Whiskey, beer, gin, booze galore,
   Were introduced to the cuspidor!

And with morning came bags of ice
   So very necessary in this life of vice;
And when I cooled my throbbing brain,
   Did I swear off and quit? No, I got soused again.

The Oregon Trail

As sung by Helen Ramsey

Way down yander in the Wahee Mountains,
    Where folks don't know about books nor countin's,
There lived a Zeke, an old galoot,
    And all he knew was how to shoot.
He had a girl and he would always tell 'er,
    Not to monkey with a city feller;
The city feller came without fail
    And old Zeke shot 'im on the Oregon Trail.

On the Oregon Trail, that's where he shot 'im;
On the Oregon Trail, they came and got 'im.
The city feller came without fail
And old Zeke shot 'im on the Oregon Trail.

Hezekiah had a lovely daughter,
    Never did a thing she hadn't oughter,
And married Zeke and they went alone
    Up in the mountains and built a home.

It wasn't long until the stork came flying,
    Brought a kid that was always crying.
The poor stork died he grew so frail,
    —Couldn't stand it on the Oregon Trail.

On the Oregon Trail that's where they killed 'im,
On the Oregon Trail a tomb they built 'im.
They dug his grave and on it wrote, "This poor bird was the family
    goat."
He carried kids until his back was broke on the Oregon Trail.

O'Slattery's Light Dragoons

You have heard of Julius Caesar and of great Napoleon, too,
And how the Cork militia beat the Turks at Waterloo.
But there's a page of glory that as yet remains uncut,
'Tis the immortal story of O'Slattery's mounted foot.

This gallant corps was organized by O'Slattery's oldest son,
A noble minded poacher with a double-breasted gun,
And many a head was broken, aye, and many an eye was shut
In learning to maneuver with O'Slattery's mounted foot.

Then down from the mountains came the squadrons and platoons,
Those four and twenty fighting men and a couple of stout gossoons.
The band was playing merrily those patriotic tunes
Secure that fame would gild the name of O'Slattery's light dragoons.

First they'd reconnoiter 'round O'Sullivan's old shabeen;
It used to be a chop-house, but we called it the canteen,
And there we saw a notice that the bravest heart unnerved:
All liquor must be settled for before the drinks are served.

So on we marched but soon again each warrior's heart turned pale,
For rising high forninst us we beheld the county jail.
And when the army faced about 'twas in time to find
A couple of policemen had surrounded it from behind.

"Across the ditch," our leader cried, "and take the foe in flank,"
But yells of consternation then arose from every rank;
For posted high upon a tree we very plainly saw:
Trespassers prosecuted in accordance with the law.

"Foiled again," cried O'Slattery, "here ends our grand campaign,
'Tis merely throwing life away to cross yon raging drain;
I'm not so bold as lions but I'm braver nor a hen,
And he who fights and runs away will live to fight again."

So back to the mountains went the squadrons and platoons,
Those four and twenty fighting men and a couple of stout gossoons.
The band was playing cautiously those patriotic tunes,
To gild the fame, tho' rather lame, of Slattery's light dragoons.

We reached the mountains safely tho' all stiff and sore with cramp,
Each took a neat of whiskey straight to dissipate the damp;
And when their pipes were loaded up O'Slattery up and said:
Today's immortal fight will be remembered by the dead.

"I never will forget," said he, "while this brave heart shall beat,
The eager way ye followed when I headed the retreat,
Ye've heard the soldier's maxim when desisting from the fight;
'Best be a coward for five minutes than a dead man all your life.'"

So there in the mountains rest the squadrons and platoons,
The four and twenty fighting men and a couple of stout gossoons.
They march no more so martially to patriotic tunes,
But all the same they sing the fame of O'Slattery's light dragoons.

Samuel Hall

As sung by the Editor

My name is Samuel Hall, Samuel Hall,
My name is Samuel Hall, and I hate you one and all;
   You're a gang of muckers all—
      Damn your eyes!

O, I killed a man 'tis said, so 'tis said,
O, I killed a man 'tis said and I smashed his bleeding head,
   And I left him lying dead—
      Damn his eyes!

So they put me into quod, into quod,
So they put me into quod with a bar and iron rod,
   And they left me there, by God—
      Damn their eyes!

O, the parson he did come, he did come,
O, the parson he did come and he looked so very glum
   As he talked of kingdom come—
      Damn his eyes!

O, the sheriff he came, too, he came, too,
O, the sheriff he came, too, with his little boys in blue
   Saying, "Sam, I'll see you through"—
      Damn his eyes!

I saw Nellie in the crowd, in the crowd,
I saw Nellie in the crowd and I shouted right out loud,
   "Say, Nellie, ain't you proud?"—
      Damn your eyes!

So a swinging up I'll go, up I'll go,
So a swinging up I'll go while you people down below
   Shout up, "Sam, I told you so."—
      Damn your eyes!

Down Among the Dead Men

Early eighteenth-century ballad attributed to John Dyer (1700–58).

Here's a health to the king and a lasting peace,
To faction an end, to wealth increase;
Come, let's drink it while we have breath,
For there's no drinking after death.
And he that will this health deny
Down among the dead men let him lie!

Let charming beauty's health go round,
In whom celestial joys are found,
And may confusion still pursue
The senseless women-hating crew;
And they that women's health deny,
Down among the dead men let them lie!

In smiling Bacchus' joys I'll roll,
Deny no pleasures to my soul;
Let Bacchus' health round briskly move,
For Bacchus is the friend of love.
And he that will this health deny,
Down among the dead men let him lie!

May love and wine their rights maintain,
And their united pleasures reign;
While Bacchus' treasure crowns the board,
We'll sing the joys that both afford;
And they that won't with us comply,
Down among the dead men let them lie!

It's the Sime the 'Ole World Over

As sung by Harrison Dowd, Provincetown, Mass., 1925

She was just a par-son's daugh-ter pure and
un - styned was her nyme, First 'e 'ad 'er then 'e
left 'er And the poor girl lost 'er nyme.

Chorus :

It's the sime the 'ole world over,
   It's the poor what tikes the blime;
It's the rich what gets the grivy,
   Aynt it all a bleedin' shime?

Then she went to London city,
   For to 'ide 'er 'orrid shime;
There she met another squire;
   Once agine she lost 'er nime.

Chorus

Look at 'im with all 'is 'orses,
   Drinking champigne in 'is club.
While the victim of 'is passions
   Drinks her guinness in a pub.

Chorus

'Ear 'im in the 'Ouse of Commons,
  Mikin' laws to put down crime;
While the womyun that 'e ruined
  'Angs 'er 'ead in wicked shime.

Chorus

See 'er in 'er 'orse and carriage,
  Drivin' d'ily through the park;
Though she's mide a wealthy marriage,
  Still she 'ides a brikin' 'eart.

Chorus

In their poor and 'umble dwelling,
  Where 'er grievin' parents live;
Drinkin' champigne that she's sent 'em,
  But they never can forgive.

Chorus

In a rose embowered cottage,
  There was born a child of sin.
But the baby had no father
  So she gently did him in.

Chorus

It's the Sime the 'Ole World Over II

There is an alarming number of variations of this little piece. Several versions found favor with the British forces during the war. An American soldier of the Seventy-Eighth Division, A. E. F., was heard singing the following:

'Ave you 'eard of Sally Carter,
Who should 'ave been Joe Johnsing's wife?
First 'e gets 'er into trou - bell,
Then he ups and tikes a knife.

"Ow, dear Joe," cries 'eart-broke Sally,
"I will be thy loving bride."
"The 'ell you, will," says Joe, and promptly
Sticks the blade in 'er inside.

Wot a 'orrid scene of terror
For to see 'er lying stiff!
Wot a funny way of ending
Just a lover's little tiff.

An' now 'e's riding in his carriage,
Passin' laws in England's nime,
While the victims of 'is passion
Creep awi' to 'ide their shime!

That Tattooed French Lady

As sung by Packey Leveson

Tune: My Home in Tennessee.

O I gi'e a shillin' to see
   That tattooed French lady.
Tattooed from head to knee
   She was a sight to see.
Right across her jaw
   Was the Royal Flying Corps;
On her back was the Union Jack,
   Now could you ask for more?

All up and down her spine
   Was a squadron all in line;
And all around her hips
   Was a fleet of battleships.
Right above one kidney
   Was a birdseye view of Sydney.
But what I liked best was across her chest,
   My home in Tennessee!

The Son of a Gambolier

I'm a rambling rake of poverty,
   From Tippery town I came.
'Twas poverty compelled me first,
   To go out in the rain;
In all sorts of weather,
   Be it wet or be it dry,
I'm bound to get my livelihood
   Or lay me down and die.

Chorus :

Then combine your humble ditties
As from inn to tavern we steer,
   Like every honest fellow
   I drinks my lager beer,
   Like every jolly fellow
   I takes my whiskey clear,
For I'm a rambling rake of poverty
The son of a son of a son of a son of a gambolier.

I once was tall and handsome,
   And was so very neat,
They thought I was too good to live,
   Most good enough to eat;
But now I'm old, my coat is torn,
   And poverty holds me fast,
And every girl turns up her nose,
   As I go wandering past.

Chorus

I'm a rambling rake of poverty,
   From Tippery town I came,
My coat I bought from an old Jew shop,
   Way down in Maiden Lane;
My hat I got from a sailor lad
   Just eighteen years ago,
And my shoes I picked from an old dust heap,
   Which every one shunned but me.

Chorus

Water Boy

As sung by James E. Harris

Water boy,
Where are you hidin'?
Ef you don' come
I'm gwine to tell yo' mammy.

Dere ain't no hammer
Dat's on dis mountain,
That rings like mine, boys,
That rings like mine.
Done bus' these rocks, boys,
From here to Macon,
All de way to the jail, boys,
Yes, back to the jail.

You, jack of diamonds,
You, jack of diamonds,
Now I know yo' of old, boy,
Yes, I know you of old.
You rob my pockets,
Yes, you rob my pockets,
You done rob my pockets
Old silver and gold.

Water boy,
Where are you hidin'?
Ef you don't come
I'm gwine to tell yo' mammy.

There Is a Tavern in the Town

As sung by Ralph Geddes

There is a tav - ern in the
town, in the town and there my dear love sits him
down, sits him down And drinks his wine 'mid
laugh-ter free, And nev - er, nev - er thinks of me.

Chorus
Fare thee well, for I must leave thee, Do not
let this part - ing grieve thee and re - mem - ber

D. C. al 𝄋

that the best of friends must part, must part.

Chorus (cont'd):

Adieu, adieu, kind friends, adieu, adieu, adieu,
I can no longer stay with you.
I'll hang my harp on a weeping willow-tree,
And may the world go well with thee.

He left me for a damsel dark, damsel dark,
Each Friday night they used to spark, used to spark,
And now my love, once true to me,
Takes that damsel on his knee.

Chorus

Oh! Dig my grave both wide and deep, wide and deep,
Put tombstones at my head and feet, head and feet,
And on my breast carve a turtle dove,
To signify I died of love.

Wal, I Swan

I run the old mill over here in Reubensville,
  My name's Joshua Ebenezer Frye;
I know a thing or two, just bet your boots I do,
  Can't fool me 'cause I'm too darn spry.
I've met your bunco men, always got the best of them;
  Once I met a couple on a Boston train.
They says, "How be you?" I says, "That'll do—
  Travel right along with your darned skinned game!"

Chorus :

Wal, I swan, I must be getting on;
  Git up, Napoleon, it looks like rain;
Wal, I'll be switched, the hay ain't pitched—
  Come in when you're over to the farm again.

I drove the old mare over to the country fair,
  Took first prize on a load of Summer squash.
Stopped at the cider mill coming over by the hill—
  Come home tighter than a drum, by gosh!
I was so darned full I gave away the old bull,
  Dropped both reins clean out on the fill;
Got home so darned late couldn't find the barn gate,
  Ma says, "Joshua, 'tain't poss-i-bill!"

Chorus

We had a big show here about a week ago,
  Pitched up a tent by the old mill dam;
Ma says, "Let's go in to see the side show—
  Just take a look at the tattooed man,"
I see a cuss look sharp at my pocketbook,
  Says, "Gimme two tens for a five?"

I says, "You darn fool, I be the constable—
   Now you're arrested sure as you're alive!"

Chorus

I drove the old bay into town yesterday,
   Hitched her up to the railroad fence;
Tied her good and strong, but a train came along—
   I ain't seen the horse or the wagon sense.
Had to foot it home, so I started off alone,
   When a man says, "Hurry, your barn's on fire!"
Wal, I had the key in my pocket, you see,
   So I knew the cuss was a fool or a liar.

Chorus

My son Joshua went to Philadelphia,
   He wouldn't do a day's work if he could;
He didn't give a darn about staying on the farm,
   What he's coming to ain't no good;
Smokes cigarettes, too, way the city folks do;
   Keep a-writin' home he's doing right well;
Seems kind of funny, but he's always out of money—
   Ma says the boy's up to some kind of hell.

Chorus

Young Charlotte

Char - lotte lived by the moun - tain side, In a
wild and drear - y spot, No oth - er house for
miles round, Be - side her fa - ther's cot.

And yet on many a wintry night,
    Young swains were gathered there;
For her father kept a festive board,
    And she was very fair.

Her father loved to see her dressed
    Gay as any city belle;
She was the only child he had
    And he loved his daughter well.

One New Year's eve as the sun went down,
    Far looked her anxious eye
As along the snowy wintry road
    The merry sleighs passed by.

In the village fifteen miles away,
    Was to be a dance that night;
Though the air without was piercing cold
    Her heart beat warm and light.

How brightly beamed her laughing eyes,
   As the well-known voice she hear'd;
As driving up to the cottage door
   Young Charles and his sleigh appeared.

"Now, Charlotte, dear," her mother said,
   "This blanket 'round you fold;
It is a terrible night without;
   You'll catch your death of cold."

"Oh, no; Oh, no!" young Charlotte cried.
   And she laughed like a gypsy queen;
"To ride in blankets muffled up
   I never can be seen.

"My silken cloak is quite enough,
   You know 'tis lined throughout;
Besides I have my silken shawl
   To tie my neck about."

Her bonnet and her gloves put on
   She jumped into the sleigh:
And they drove down the mountainside
   And over the hills away.

There's life in the music of the merry bells,
   As over the hills they go;
Such a creaking sound the runners make
   As they crease the frozen snow.

With muffled faces tied about,
   Five miles at length were passed.
When Charles with few and shivering words
   Their silence broke at last.

"Such a dreadful night I never knew,
   My reins I scarce can hold."

Young Charlotte shivering feebly said,
  "I am exceeding cold."

He cracked his whip, he urged his steeds,
  Much faster than before.
And thus five more dreary miles
  In silence they passed o'er.

"How fast," says Charles, "the freezing ice
  Is gathering on my brow."
And Charlotte still more weakly said,
  "I'm getting warmer now."

And on they rode through the frosty air
  And the glittering cold starlight,
Until at last the village lights
  And the ballroom were in sight.

They reached the hall and Charles jumped out,
  And reached his hand for her.
Saying, "Why sit there like a monument
  That has no power to stir?"

He called her once, he called her twice,
  But she answered not a word.
He called for her again and again,
  But still she never stirred.

He took her hand in his. Oh, God!
  'Twas cold and hard as stone.
He tore the shawl from off her brow,
  Cold sweat upon there shone.

Then quickly to the lighted hall
  Her lifeless form he bore;
Young Charlotte was a frozen corpse,
  And danced she never more.

Then he sat himself down by her side,
    While bitter tears did flow.
He cried, "My own, my promised bride,
    I never more shall know."

He put his arms around her neck
    And kissed her marble brow;
His thoughts went back to where she said,
    "I'm growing warmer now."

'Twas then the cruel monster, Death,
    Was claiming her as his own;
Young Charlotte's eyes were closed,
    Poor Charles was all alone.

Then he bore her back to the sleigh,
    And with her he rode home;
And when he reached the cottage door
    Oh, how her parents mourned.

Her parents wept for their daughter dear,
    And Charles mourned in the gloom,
Till at last young Charles, too, died of grief,
    And they both rest in one tomb.

Young ladies, think of this dear girl
    And always dress aright,
And never venture so thinly clad
    Into the wintry night.

Whiskey for My Johnny

As sung by one who knew and loved his rye on board the
Diesel Ship Glenpool, *August, 1915*

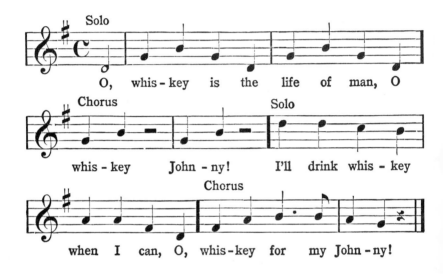

I'll drink whiskey when I can,
   O, whiskey, Johnny!
Whiskey from an old tin can,
   O, whiskey for my Johnny!

I drink it hot, I drink it cold,
   O, whiskey, Johnny!
I drink it new, I drink it old,
   O, whiskey for my Johnny!

Whiskey makes me feel so glad,
   O, whiskey, Johnny!
Whiskey killed my poor old dad,
   O, whiskey for my Johnny!

I Wish I Was Single Again

When I was single, Oh, then, Oh, then,
When I was single, Oh, then,
When I was single,
My money did jingle,
I wish I was single again, again,
I wish I was single again.

I married me a wife, Oh, then, Oh, then,
I married me a wife, Oh, then,
I married me a wife,
She's the plague of my life,
And I wished I was single again, again,
I wished I was single again.

My wife she died, Oh, then, Oh, then,
My wife she died, Oh, then,
My wife she died,
And then I cried,
To think I was single again, again,
To think I was single again.

I married another, the devil's grandmother,
I wished I was single again,
For when I was single,
My money did jingle,
I wish I was single again, again,
I wish I was single again.

Rolling Home

As sung by the crew of the S.S. Standard, *May, 1915*

Call all hands to man the cap-stan, See the
ca - ble run down clear, Heave a - way, and with a
will, boys, For old En - gland we will
steer; And we'll sing in joy - ful cho-rus In the
watch - es of the night, And we'll sight the shores of
Eng-land When the gray dawn brings the light.

Roll - ing home, roll - ing home, roll - ing home a - cross the sea; Roll - ing home to mer-rie En - gland, Roll - ing home, dear land, to thee.

Call all hands to man the capstan,
   See the cable run down clear,
Heave away, and with a will, boys,
   For old England we will steer;
And we'll sing in jolly chorus
   In the watches of the night,
And we'll sight the shores of England
   When the gray dawn brings the light.

Rolling home, rolling home,
Rolling home across the sea;
Rolling home to dear old England,
Rolling home, dear land, to thee.

Up aloft amid the rigging,
   Blows the loud exultant gale,
Like a bird's out-stretched pinions
   Spreads on high each swelling sail;
And the wild waves cleft behind us,
   Seem to murmur as they flow,

There are loving hearts that wait you
  In the land to which you go.

Rolling home, etc.

Many thousand miles behind us,
  Many thousand miles before,
Ancient ocean heaves to waft us
  To the well-remembered shore.
Cheer up, Jack, bright smiles await you
  From the fairest of the fair,
And her loving eyes will greet you
  With kind welcomes everywhere.

Oh! Oh! Oh! It's a Lovely War!

Up to your waist in water,
Up to your eyes in slush,
Using the kind of language
That makes the sergeants blush;
Who wouldn't join the army,
That's what we all enquire,
Don't we pity the poor civilians
Sitting beside the fire?

Chorus :

Oh! Oh! Oh! It's a lovely war,
Who wouldn't be a soldier, eh?
Oh, it's a shame to take the pay.

As soon as reveille has gone
We feel just as heavy as lead,
But we never get up till the sergeant
Brings our breakfast up to bed.

What do you want with eggs and ham
When you've got plum and apple jam?
Form fours! Right turn!
How shall we spend the money we earn?

Chorus

When does a soldier grumble?
When does a soldier make a fuss?
No one is more contented
In all the world than us.
Oh, it's a cushy life, boys,
Really, we love it so;
Once a fellow was sent on leave
And simply refused to go.

Chorus

Come to the cook-house door, boys,
Sniff at the lovely stew,
Who is it says the colonel gets
Better grub than you?
Any complaints this morning?
Do we complain? Not we.
What's the matter with lumps of onion
Floating around the tea?

Chorus

Maid of Amsterdam

Solo

In Am - ster - dam there dwelt a maid—Mark
well what I do say. In Am - ster-dam there
dwelt a maid, And she was mis-tress of her trade.
I'll go no more a - rov - ing with you fair

Chorus

maid. A - rov - ing, a - rov - ing, Since

rov-ing's been my ru - in, I'll go no more a -

rov - ing with you fair maid.

Her eyes were blue, her cheeks were red,
   Mark well what I do say.
Her eyes were blue, her cheeks were red;
   A wealth of hair was on her head.
I'll go no more a-roving with you, fair maid.

Chorus

I put my arm around her waist,
   Mark well what I do say,
I put my arm around her waist;
   Says she, "Young man, you're in some haste."
I'll go no more a-roving with you, fair maid.

Chorus

I took that girl upon my knee,
   Mark well what I do say.
I took that girl upon my knee;
   Says she, "Young man, you're rather free."
I'll go no more a-roving with you, fair maid.

Chorus

Mademoiselle from Armentieres

(Fragmentary)

Mad-em-o'-elle from Ar-men-tieres par - - lez

vous.... Mad - em - ois - elle from   Ar-men-tieres

par - - lez vous..... Mad - em - ois - elle from

Ar - men-tiers. She has - n't been kissed in for - ty

years. Hink - y dink - y par - lez vous.........

Mademoiselle all dressed in white, parlez vous. . . .
Mademoiselle all dressed in white, parlez vous. . . .
    Mademoiselle all dressed in black
    'Cause her Yankee didn't come back,
Hinky dinky, parlez vous.

O, the French they are a funny race, etc.
    They swipe your francs
    And lie to your face, etc.

The little marine he grew and grew, etc.
And now he's hugging and kissing 'em too, etc.

The little marine he grew and grew, etc.
And now he's part of the army too, etc.

Froggie, have you some very good wine? etc.
Fit for a bum right out of the line, etc.

Froggie, have you a daughter fine? etc.
Fit for a marine just out of the line, etc.

O, oui, I have a daughter fine, etc.
But not for a Yankee just out of the line, etc.

Froggie, have you a daughter fine, etc.
Fit for a doughboy up in the line, etc.

O, oui, I have a daughter fine, etc.
Fit for a Yankee up in the line, etc.

The little Yankee went over the top, etc.
He didn't know when the hell to stop, etc.

The little marine in love with his nurse, parlez vous. . . .
The little marine in love with his nurse, parlez vous. . . .
   The little marine in love with his nurse,
   He's taken her now for better or worse,
Hinky dinky, parlez vous. . . .

The Cowboy's Lament

*Version by Frank A. Lomax**

As I walked out in the streets of Laredo,
As I walked out in Laredo one day,
I spied a poor cowboy wrapped up in white linen,
Wrapped up in white linen as cold as the clay.

"Oh, beat the drum slowly and play the fife lowly,
Play the Dead March as you carry me along;
Take me to the green valley, there lay the sod o'er me,
For I'm a young cowboy and I know I've done wrong."

"I see by your outfit that you are a cowboy,"
These words he did say as I boldly stepped by.
"Come sit down beside me and hear my sad story;
I was shot in the breast and I know I must die."

"Let sixteen gamblers come handle my coffin,
Let sixteen cowboys come sing me a song,
Take me to the graveyard and lay the sod o'er me,
For I'm a poor cowboy and I know I've done wrong."

"My friends and relations they live in the Nation,
They know not where their boy has gone.
He first came to Texas and hired to a ranchman,
Oh, I'm a young cowboy and I know I've done wrong."

"Go write a letter to my gray-haired mother,
And carry the same to my sister so dear;
But not a word of this shall you mention
When a crowd gathers round you my story to hear."

"Then beat your drum slowly and play your fife lowly,
Beat the Dead March as you carry me along;
We all love our cowboys so young and so handsome,
We all love our cowboys although they've done wrong."

*From *Cowboy Songs* published by Macmillan Company.

"There is another more dear than a sister,
She'll bitterly weep when she hears I am gone.
There is another who will win her affections,
For I'm a young cowboy and they say I've done wrong."

"Go gather around you a crowd of young cowboys,
And tell them the story of this my sad fate;
Tell one and the other before they go further
To stop their wild roving before 'tis too late."

"Oh, muffle your drums, then play your fifes merrily;
Play the Dead March as you go along.
And fire your guns right over my coffin;
There goes an unfortunate boy to his home."

"It was once in the saddle I used to go dashing,
It was once in the saddle I used to go gay;
First to the dram-house, then to the card-house,
Got shot in the breast, I am dying to-day."

"Get six jolly cowboys to carry my coffin;
Get six pretty maidens to bear up my pall.
Put bunches of roses all over my coffin,
Put roses to deaden the clods as they fall."

"Then swing your rope slowly and rattle your spurs lowly,
And give a wild whoop as you carry me along;
And in the grave throw me and roll the sod o'er me,
For I'm a young cowboy and I know I've done wrong."

"Go bring me a cup, a cup of cold water,
To cool my parched lips," the cowboy said;
Before I turned, the spirit had left him
And gone to its Giver,—the cowboy was dead.

We beat the drum slowly and played the fife lowly,
And bitterly wept as we bore him along;
For we all loved our comrade, so brave, young and handsome,
We all loved our comrade although he'd done wrong.

The Face on the Bar-room Floor

By Hugh D'Arcy

'Twas a balmy summer evening, and a goodly crowd was there,
Which well-nigh filled Joe's bar-room, on the corner of the square;
And as songs and witty stories came through the open door,
A vagabond crept slowly in and posed upon the floor.

"Where did it come from?" someone said. "The wind has blown it in."
"What does it want?" another cried. "Some whiskey, rum or gin?"
"Here, Toby, sic 'em, if your stomach's equal to the work—
I wouldn't touch him with a fork, he's filthy as a Turk."

This badinage the poor wretch took with stoical good grace;
In fact, he smiled as tho' he thought he'd struck the proper place.
"Come, boys, I know there's kindly hearts among so good a crowd—
To be in such good company would make a deacon proud."

"Give me a drink—that's what I want—I'm out of funds, you know,
When I had the cash to treat the gang this hand was never slow.
What? You laugh as if you thought this pocket never held a sou;
I once was fixed as well, my boys, as any one of you."

"There, thanks, that's braced me nicely; God bless you one and all;
Next time I pass this good saloon I'll make another call.
Give you a song? No, I can't do that; my singing days are past;
My voice is cracked, my throat's worn out, and my lungs are going fast."

"I'll tell you a funny story, and a fact, I promise, too,
Say! Give me another whiskey, and I'll tell you what I'll do—
That ever I was a decent man not one of you would think;
But I was, some four or five years back. Say, give me another drink."

"Fill her up, Joe, I want to put some life into my frame—
Such little drinks to a bum like me are miserably tame;
Five fingers—there, that's the scheme—and corking whiskey, too.
Well, here's luck, boys, and landlord, my best regards to you.

"You've treated me pretty kindly and I'd like to tell you how
I came to be the dirty sot you see before you now.
As I told you, once I was a man, with muscle, frame and health,
And but for a blunder ought to have made considerable wealth.

"I was a painter—not one that daubed on bricks and wood,
But an artist, and for my age, was rated pretty good.
I worked hard at my canvas, and was bidding fair to rise,
For gradually I saw the star of fame before my eyes.

"I made a picture perhaps you've seen, 'tis called the 'Chase of Fame.'
It brought me fifteen hundred pounds and added to my name.
And then I met a woman—now comes the funny part—
With eyes that petrified my brain, and sunk into my heart.

"Why don't you laugh? 'Tis funny that the vagabond you see
Could ever love a woman, and expect her love for me;
But 'twas so, and for a month or two, her smiles were freely given.
And when her loving lips touched mine, it carried me to heaven.

"Boys, did you ever see a girl for whom your soul you'd give,
With a form like the Milo Venus, too beautiful to live;
With eyes that would beat the Koh-i-noor, and a wealth of chestnut
     hair?
If so, 'twas she, for there never was another half so fair.

"I was working on a portrait, one afternoon in May,
Of a fair-haired boy, a friend of mine, who lived across the way;
And Madeline admired it, and, much to my surprise,
She said she'd like to know the man that had such dreamy eyes.

"It didn't take long to know him, and before the month had flown
My friend had stole my darling, and I was left alone;
And ere a year of misery had passed above my head,
The jewel I had treasured so had tarnished and was dead.

"That's why I took to drink, boys. Why, I never saw you smile,
I thought you'd be amused, and laughing all the while.
Why, what's the matter, friend? There's a tear-drop in your eye.
Come, laugh like me; 'tis only babes and women that should cry.

"Say, boys, if you give me just another whiskey I'll be glad,
And I'll draw right here a picture of the face that drove me mad.
Give me that piece of chalk with which you mark the baseball score—
You shall see the lovely Madeline upon the bar-room floor."

Another drink, and with chalk in hand, the vagabond began
To sketch a face that might well buy the soul of any man.
Then, as he placed another lock upon the shapely head,
With a fearful shriek, he leaped and fell across the picture—dead.

Twenty Years Ago

As sung by Helen Ramsey

Twenty years ago today,
The yellow sun was settin'.
A soldier boy marched to the fray
And left his parents frettin'.
He said, "Good-bye, my mother dear,
I'm goin' off to fight,
If I'm not home tomorrow,
I may not be home tonight."

"Oh, mother, say good-bye for me
To little Mollie Humphrey,
I hear the bugles callin'
And I must fight for my country."

Yo ho for the land he loves so well,
He fought with a slide trombone.
The horn was too low,
And caught in his toe,
It tripped him and he fell.

"Who'll save the flag!" the general cried.
"I will," replied a stranger.
"Although I promised mother
I'd not go near any danger."
Our soldier boy jumped up and cried,
"You shall not go alone,
For I will accompany you
Upon my slide trombone."

A cruel cannon it came up
And shot his legs away;
But he kept rushin' onward
In the middle of the fray.

Yo ho for the land he loved so well,
He fought in his suit of blue.
Though only a musician,
It shows his ambition
For the land he loved so well.

Lasca

By Frank Desprez

Recited with gestures, by Fern Forrester Shay

I want free life, and I want fresh air,
And I sigh for the canter after the cattle,
The crack of the whip like shots in a battle,
The melee of horns and hoofs and heads
That wars and wrangles and scatters and spreads,
The green beneath and the blue above,
And dash and danger, and life and love,
And Lasca!

     Lasca used to ride
On a mouse-gray mustang close to my side,
With blue serape and bright-belled spur;
I laughed with joy as I looked at her!
Little knew she of books or of creeds;
An Ave Maria sufficed her needs;
Little she cared save to be by my side,
To ride with me and ever to ride,
From San Saba's shore to Lavaca's tide.
She was as bold as the billows that beat,
She was as wild as the breezes that blow;
From her little head to her little feet
She was swayed in her suppleness to and fro
By each gust of passion; a sapling pine,
That grows on the edge of a Kansas bluff,
And wars with the wind when the weather is rough,
Is like Lasca, this love of mine.
She would hunger, that I might eat,
Would take the bitter and leave me the sweet.
But once, when I made her jealous, for fun,
At something I'd whispered or looked or done,
One Sunday, in San Antonio,

To a glorious girl on the Alamo,
She drew from her garter a dear little dagger,
And sting of a wasp!—it made me stagger!
An inch to the left or an inch to the right,
And I shouldn't be maundering here tonight;
But she sobbed, and sobbing, so swiftly bound
Her torn *rebozo* about the wound,
That I quite forgave her. Scratches don't count
        In Texas, down by the Rio Grande.

Her eye was brown—a deep, deep brown;
Her hair was darker than her eye;
And something in her smile and frown,
Curled crimson lip and instep high,
Showed that there ran in each blue vein,
Mixed with the milder Aztec strain,
The vigorous vintage of old Spain.
She was alive in every limb
With feeling, to the finger tips;
And when the sun is like a fire,
And sky one shining, soft sapphire
One does not drink in little sips.

  .   .   .   .   .

The air was heavy, the night was hot,
I sat by her side and forgot—forgot;
Forgot the herd that were taking their rest,
Forgot that the air was close, opprest;
That the Texas norther comes sudden and soon,
In the dead of night or the blaze of noon;
That, once let the herd at its breath take fright,
Nothing on earth can stop the flight;
And woe to the rider and woe to the steed
Who falls in front of their mad stampede!

  .   .   .   .   .

Was that thunder? I grasped the cord
Of my swift mustang without a word.
I sprang to the saddle, and she clung behind,
Away! on a hot chase down the wind
But never was foxhunt half so hard,
And never was steed so little spared;
For we rode for our lives. You shall hear how we fared,
      In Texas, down by the Rio Grande.

The mustang flew, and we urged him on;
There was one chance left, and you have but one—
Halt, jump to ground and shoot your horse;
Crouch under his carcase and take your chance;
And if the steers in their frantic course
Don't batter you both to pieces at once,
You may thank your star; if not, goodby
To the quickening kiss and the long-drawn sigh
And the open air and the open sky,
      In Texas, down by the Rio Grande.

The cattle gained on us, and, just as I felt
For my old six-shooter behind in my belt,
Down came the mustang, and down came we
Clinging together, and—what was the rest?
A body that spread itself on my breast,
Two arms that shielded my dizzy head,
Two lips that hard on my lips were prest;
Then came thunder in my ears,
As over us surged the sea of steers,
Blows that beat blood into my eyes
And when I could rise—
Lasca was dead!

I gouged out a grave a few feet deep,
And there in earth's arms I laid her to sleep;
And there she is lying, and no one knows,
And the Summer shines and the Winter snows;

For many a day the flowers have spread
A pall of petals over her head,
And the little gray hawk hangs aloft in the air,
And the sly coyote trots here and there,
And the black snake glides and glitters and slides
Into a rift in a cottonwood tree;
And the buzzard sails on,
And comes, and is gone,
Stately and still, like a ship at sea.
And I wonder why I do not care
For the things that are, like the things that were,
Does half my heart lie buried there,
        In Texas, down by the Rio Grande?

'Ostler Joe

By George R. Sims

I stood at eve where the sun went down,
  By a grave where a woman lies,
Who lured men's souls to the shores of sin
  With the light of her wanton eyes;
Who sang the song that the siren sang
  On the treacherous Lorelei height,
Whose face was as fair as a Summer's day
  And whose heart was as black as night.

Yet a blossom I fain would pluck to-day
  From the garden above her dust—
Not the languorous lily of soulless sin,
  Nor the blood-red rose of lust—
But a sweet white blossom of holy love
  That grew in that one green spot
In the arid desert of Phryne's life,
  Where all else was parched and hot.

In the Summer, when the meadows
  Were aglow with blue and red,
Joe, the 'ostler of "The Magpie,"
  And fair Annie Smith were wed.
Plump was Annie, plump and pretty,
  With a face as fair as snow;
He was anything but handsome,
  Was the "Magpie's" 'ostler Joe.

But he won the winsome lassie;
  They'd a cottage and a cow—
And her matronhood sat lightly
  On the village beauty's brow.

Sped the months, and came a baby—
  Such a blue-eyed baby boy,
Joe was working in the stables
  When they told him of his joy.

He was rubbing down the horses—
  Gave them, then and there,
All a special feed of clover,
  Just in honor of his heir.
It had been his great ambition
  (And he told the horses so)
That the fates would send a baby
  Who might bear the name of Joe.

Little Joe, the child was christened,
  And like babies grew apace.
He'd his mother's eyes of azure
  And his father's honest face.
Swift the happy years went over,
  Years of blue and cloudless sky;
Love was lord of that small cottage
  And the tempest passed them by.

Down the lane by Annie's cottage
  Chanced a gentleman to roam;
He caught a glimpse of Annie
  In her bright and happy home.
Thrice he came and saw her sitting
  By the window with her child,
And he nodded to the baby,
  And the baby laughed and smiled.

So at last it grew to know him
  (Little Joe was nearly four),
He would call the pretty "gemplum"
  As he passed the open door.

And one day he ran and caught him,
  And in child's play pulled him in;
And the baby Joe had prayed for
  Brought about the mother's sin.

'Twas the same old wretched story,
  That for ages bards have sung;
'Twas a woman, weak and wanton,
  And a villain's tempting tongue;
'Twas a picture deftly painted
  For a silly creature's eyes,
Of the Babylonian wonders
  And the joy that in them lies.

Annie listened and was tempted—
  Was tempted and she fell,
As the angels fell from Heaven
  To the blackest depths of Hell.
She was promised wealth and splendor
  And a life of genteel sloth;
Yellow gold, for child and husband—
  And the woman left them both.

Home one eve came Joe, the 'ostler,
  With a cheery cry of "Wife!"
Finding that which blurred forever
  All the story of his life.
She had left a silly letter,
  Through the cruel scrawl he spelt,
Then he sought the lonely bedroom,
  Joined his horny hands and knelt.

"Now, O Lord, O God, forgive her,
  For she ain't to blame," he cried;
"For I ought to seen her trouble
  And a-gone away and died.

Why a girl like her—God bless her—
    T'wasn't likely as she'd rest
With her bonny head forever
    On a 'ostler's ragged vest."

"It was kind o' her to bear with me
    All the long and happy time;
So, for my sake please to bless her,
    Though you count her deed a crime.
If so be I don't pray proper,
    Lord, forgive me, for you see,
I can talk all right to 'osses,
    But I'm kind o' strange with Thee."

Ne'er a line came to the cottage
    From the woman who had flown;
Joe, the baby, died that Winter,
    And the man was left alone.
Ne'er the bitter word he uttered,
    But in silence kissed the rod,
Saving what he told his horses,
    Saving what he told to God.

Far away in mighty London
    Rose the wanton into fame,
For her beauty was men's homage,
    And she prospered in her shame.
Quick from lord to lord she flitted,
    Higher still each prize she won,
And her rivals paled beside her
    As the stars beside the sun.

Next she trod the stage half naked,
    And she dragged Art's temple down
To the level of a market
    For the women of the town.

And the kisses she had given
　　To poor 'ostler Joe for naught
With their gold and precious jewels
　　Rich and titled roués bought.

Went the years with flying footsteps
　　While her star was at its height:
Then the darkness came on swiftly
　　And the gloaming turned to night.
Shattered strength and faded beauty
　　Tore the laurels from her brow;
Of the thousands who had worshipped
　　Never one came near her now.

Broken down in health and fortune,
　　Men forgot her very name,
Till the news that she was dying
　　Woke the echoes of her fame,
And the papers in their gossip
　　Mentioned how an actress lay
Sick to death in humble lodgings,
　　Growing weaker every day.

One there was who read the story
　　In a far-off country place;
And that night the dying woman
　　Woke and looked upon his face.
Once again the strong arms clasped her
　　That had clasped her long ago,
And the weary head lay pillowed
　　On the breast of 'ostler Joe.

All the past he had forgiven—
　　All the sorrow and the shame;
He had found her sick and lonely
　　And his wife he now could claim.

Since the grand folks who had known her
 One and all had slunk away,
He could clasp his long-lost darling,
 And no man could say him nay.

In his arms death found her lying,
 From his arms her spirit fled,
And his tears came down in torrents
 As he knelt beside his dead.
Never once his love had faltered
 Through her sad, unhallowed life,
And the stone above her ashes
 Bears the sacred name of wife.

That's the blossom I fain would pluck today
 From the garden above her dust;
Not the languorous lily of soulless sin
 Nor the blood-red rose of lust,
But a sweet white blossom of holy love
 That grew in the one green spot
In the arid desert of Phryne's life,
 Where all else was parched and hot.

The Kid's Fight

Us two was pals, the Kid and me;
'Twould cut no ice if some gayzee,
As tough as hell jumped either one,
We'd both light in and hand him some.

Both of a size, the Kid and me,
We tipped the scales at thirty-three;
And when we'd spar 'twas give and take,
I wouldn't slug for any stake.

One day we worked out at the gym,
Some swell guy hangin' round called "Slim,"
Watched us and got stuck on the Kid,
Then signed him up, that's what he did.

This guy called "Slim" he owned a string
Of lightweights, welters, everything;
He took the Kid out on the road,
And where they went none of us knowed.

I guessed the Kid had changed his name,
And fightin' the best ones in the game.
I used to dream of him at night,
No letters came—he couldn't write.

In just about two months or three
I signed up with Bucktooth McGee.
He got me matched with Denver Brown,
I finished him in half a round.

Next month I fought with Brooklyn Mike,
As tough a boy who hit the pike;
Then Frisco Jim and Battlin' Ben,
And knocked them all inside of ten.

I took 'em all and won each bout,
None of them birds could put me out;
The sportin' writers watched me slug,
Then all the papers run my mug.

"He'd rather fight than eat," they said.
"He's got the punch, he'll knock 'em dead."
There's only one I hadn't met,
That guy they called "The Yorkshire Pet."

He'd cleaned 'em all around in France,
No one in England stood a chance;
And I was champ in U.S.A.,
And knocked 'em cuckoo every day.

Now all McGee and me could think
Was how we'd like to cross the drink,
And knock this bucko for a row,
And grab a wagon load of dough.

At last Mac got me matched all right,
Five thousand smackers for the fight;
Then me and him packed up our grip,
And went to grab that championship.

I done some trainin' and the night
Set for the battle sure was right;
The crowd was wild, for this here bout
Was set to last till one was out.

The mob went crazy when the Pet
Came in, I'd never seen him yet;
And then I climbed up through the ropes,
All full of fight and full of hopes.

The crowd gave me an awful yell,
('Twas even money at the bell)
They stamped their feet and shook the place;
The Pet turned 'round, I saw his face!

My guts went sick that's what they did,
For Holy Gee, it was the Kid!
We just had time for one good shake,
We meant it, too, it wasn't fake.

Whang! went the bell, the fight was on,
I clinched until the round was gone,
A-beggin, that he'd let me take
The fall for him—he wouldn't fake.

Hell, no, the Kid was on the square,
And said we had to fight it fair,
The crowd had bet their dough on us—
We had to fight (the honest cuss).

The referee was yellin' "break,"
The crowd was sore and howlin' "fake."
They'd paid their dough to see a scrap.
And so far we'd not hit a tap.

The second round we both begin.
I caught a fast one on my chin;
And stood like I was in a doze,
Until I got one on the nose.

I started landin' body blows,
He hooked another on my nose,
That riled my fightin' blood like hell,
And we was sluggin' at the bell.

The next round started, from the go
The millin' we did wasn't slow,
I landed hard on him, and then,
He took the count right up to ten.

He took the limit on one knee,
A chance to get his wind and see;
At ten he jumped up like a flash
And on my jaw he hung a smash.

I'm fightin', too, there, toe to toe,
And hittin' harder, blow for blow,
I damn soon knowed he couldn't stay,
He rolled his eyes—you know the way.

The way he staggered made me sick,
I stalled, McGee yelled "cop him quick!"
The crowd was wise and yellin' "fake,"
They'd seen the chance I wouldn't take.

The mob kept tellin' me to land,
And callin' things I couldn't stand;
I stepped in close and smashed his chin,
The Kid fell hard; he was all in.

I carried him into his chair,
And tried to bring him to for fair,
I rubbed his wrists, done everything,
A doctor climbed into the ring.

And I was scared as I could be,
The Kid was starin' and couldn't see;
The doctor turned and shook his head,
I looked again—the Kid was dead!

Don't Go in them Lions' Cage Tonight, Mother

As sung by Lawrence Grant and W. D. Smith

To be half-recited, half sung in a cross between a childish treble and a whiskey tenor to any melody you can adapt to the words. It is quite effective at certain stages.

A lady once she had a lovely daughter,
    The lady was an actress on the stage.
She traveled with a troupe of awful lions,
    And each night she went in them lions' cage.
One night the daughter had a premonition
    That everything that night would not be right,
And so she told her mother in the kitchen,
    "Oh, don't go near them lions' cage tonight!"

Chorus :

    "Oh, don't go near them lions' cage,
        Dear mother, dear, tonight.
        Them lions am ferocious and might bite!
        And when they get them angry fits
        They'll chew you into little bits.
        Oh, don't go near them lions' cage tonight."

The lady laughed "ha ha!" she did not heed the warning
    That unto her her daughter she did give.
"Oh, no," she cried, "I do not fear them lions:
    Not one of them could make me cease to live."
She went into that cage of awful lions,
    Them lions were ferocious as could be.
"Alas," she cried, as one strode up and bit her,
    "I now recall what daughter said to me."

Chorus

"Oh, who will save my mother?" cried the daughter.
  "By lions she is being bit and et!"
"I will," replied a young man in the gallery;
  "I'll save your mother from them brutes, you bet!"
He went into that cage of awful lions,
  Of lion biting she was almost dead.
"Here is your ma," he said to her and kissed her;
  For he the daughter loved and soon did wed.

The High Barbaree

Heard on board the S.S. Standard *while afire off Yucatan,*
May 11, 1915

There were two loft - y ships   from   old   Eng - land

came   Blow   high,   blow   low,   and

so sailed we: One was the Prince of

Lu - ther, and the oth - er Prince of Wales, Cruis-ing

down a - long the coast of the High Bar - bar - ee.

"Aloft there, aloft!" our jolly boatswain cries,
Blow high, blow low, and so sailed we;
"Look ahead, look astern, look a-weather and a-lee,
Look along down the coast of the High Barbaree."

"There's nought upon the stern, there's nought upon the lee,"
Blow high, blow low, and so sailed we;
"But there's a lofty ship to windward, and she's sailing fast and free,
Sailing down along the coast of the High Barbaree."

"O hail her, O hail her," our gallant captain cried,
Blow high, blow low, and so sailed we;
"Are you a man-o'-war or a privateer," said he,
"Cruising down along the coast of the High Barbaree?"

"O, I am not a man-o'-war nor privateer," said he,
Blow high, blow low, and so sailed we;
"But I'm a salt-sea pirate a-looking for my fee,
Cruising down along the coast of the High Barbaree."

O, 'twas broadside to broadside a long time we lay,
Blow high, blow low, and so sailed we;
Until the "Prince of Luther" shot the pirate's masts away,
Cruising down along the coast of the High Barbaree.

"O quarter, O quarter," those pirates then did cry,
Blow high, blow low, and so sailed we;
But the quarter that we gave them—we sunk them in the sea,
Cruising down along the coast of the High Barbaree.

The Marines' Song

From the Halls of Montezuma
  To the shores of Tripoli,
We fight our country's battles,
  On the land as on the sea.
Admiration of the Nation,
  We're the finest ever seen,
And we glory in the title :
  The United States Marine.

From the Pest Hole of Cavite
  To the Ditch at Panama,
You will find them very needy
  Of marines.   That's what we are.
We're the watch-dogs of a pile of coal,
  Or we dig a magazine.
Though our job lots are quite manifold,
  Who would not be a marine ?

Our flag's unfurled to every breeze,
  From dawn to setting sun ;
We've fought in every clime and place
  Where we could take a gun.
In the snows of far-off northern lands
  And in sunny tropic scenes,
You will always find us on the job,
  The United States Marines.

Here's health to you and to our corps,
  Which we are proud to serve :
In many a strife we have fought for life
  And never lost our nerve.

If the Army and the Navy
  Ever look on Heaven's scenes,
They will find the streets are guarded
  By the United States Marines.

MORE PIOUS FRIENDS AND DRUNKEN COMPANIONS

SONGS AND BALLADS OF CONVIVIALITY
Collected by
FRANK SHAY

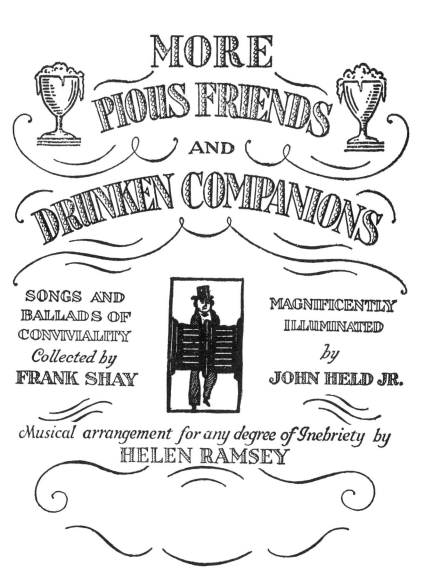

MAGNIFICENTLY ILLUMINATED
by
JOHN HELD JR.

Musical arrangement for any degree of Inebriety by
HELEN RAMSEY

The DEAR DEAD DAYS

WHEN A GIRL DRANK BEER AND LIKED IT
ENG. BY JOHN. HELD JR WITH THE LAUGH ON THE OTHER SIDE OF HIS FACE – – ·

This Book is Dedicated in General
to
The Society of the Forty Pious Friends
The International Bar Flies
The Amalgamated Order of Beer Shifters
The Barroom Boys and Girls
The Elite Order of Bung Starters
The Three Hours for Lunch Club
La Société des 40 Hommes et 8 Cheveaux
The Stowaways of New York
The Fraternal Order of Billy Goats
The Beachcombers of Provincetown
To Most of the Elks and Some of the Knights
To all Newspapermen Who Would be Great Writers
if They Could Leave the Stuff Alone
To That Great Army Who, Drunk or Sober, Love to Sing the
Old Songs of a Very Dear and Departed Era
And in Particular to
The Honorable Louis Bret Hart, of Buffalo.

NELL WAS THE BEST THE CAMP PRODUCED

ENGRAVED BY JOHN HELD JR. AN ENGRAVER OF THE OLD SCHOOL

Here's To Crime

The songs brought together in this second collection are, like their predecessors, snatched for the most part from a more beery and hilarious age. Some have the flavor of yesterday's bar-rag while others seem to have been brought into being by the ladies and gentlemen of the Anti-Saloon League. Some are frankly convivial and will serve as a goad to memories more tenacious than that of the editor. Others are merely the dolorous ballads sung by whiskey johnnies when in their cups. All of them have been tried out under the most exacting conditions and found not entirely wanting.

Since the first volume appeared there has been formed the Society of the Forty Pious Friends whose sole and main endeavor will be to seek out the songs of the dear, departed days and put them into practical use by keeping them alive for that future generation who, it is hoped, will throw off the shackles of sobriety that bind us. The society has endowed a completely equipped barroom from the swinging doors to the old third rail. The chief bartender is concert-meister and when the Board of Examination and Eligibility is completely and properly oiled he will give the word to the First Ivory Thumper. If the song proves acceptable under such conditions it will be placed in the society's repertory. For safety's sake the location of this laboratory must remain a secret.

Booze, under the present régime, has come out of the hell-holes and been given an honorable place in the American home. If the quality had only held up there would be but little room for complaint. The stuff they serve these days is terrible: there isn't a song in a boat-load. In the old days Father got his load at the corner. If it was that kind of a load he sang; if it wasn't he staggered a little. Mother knew by the tremolo of his voice or the footsteps on the stair that Father was not traveling on an even keel and herded the children out of the way until Daddy and his parcel were tucked into bed. Now Father is setting a bad example for the whole family by keeping the bottle under the kitchen sink where it will be handy. And when Mother feels a bit low she takes a shot of tiger milk and feels a lot better for a few moments. Joe, the eldest boy, who under normal conditions would be a tee-totaler until he was twenty-one, is not above pepping up his style with a jolt from the brew. Mamie, who is in business college, shows her young man that she knows how matters stand by slipping him a night-cap as he leaves.

Time was when the young man who occasionally took a drink called on his girl friend he was very careful to chew a clove or sen-sen to disguise his breath: he was careful not to let the aroma cross her nose. Today what happens? He calls on the girl and makes no effort to conceal the fact he has had a drink. The girl, if she is experienced, sets out a couple of glasses and a bottle of dry ginger ale. Has the young man appeared with nothing more than a breath? He is an inconsiderate fool, a stupid yokel, and the door is held open for him.

Travelers who have covered these states within the last few months tell us that nowhere have they found what is happily called "the dry sentiment." Is this phrase merely a device of the reformers and politicians? Well-known writers, several of them Englishmen, who have gone on extended lecture tours and who have been guests in the most American of homes, say they are always greeted with cocktails and that whichever way they turn they run into someone with a shaker who is just issuing dividends. In a very wide circle of friends the nearest to a total abstainer is one who is off the stuff temporarily for his health. The phrase, "No, I never touch a drop," went out with the Gibson girl.

What disturbs the ballad-monger is that there is less singing than ever. This may be due to the quality of the liquor we are throwing into us, for it is sodden stuff, or it may be due to the neighbors. What this country needs is a singing Lindbergh to make it "singing-minded" or a constitutional enactment absolutely prohibiting the singing of any but revival numbers. We need someone to lead us out of the boozy silence into which we have sunk. Those who have tried it know that a drink with a song is twice a drink.

A few of the hundreds who have written the editor since the first volume appeared seem to take it for granted that our home is one of hell's gaudy palaces, that we are a hell-roaring wild cat who each night makes the welkin ring with bawdy songs, that we are sold body and soul to the saloon interests. Such we regret is not the case though we must confess to a great longing to be all those things. Rather are we the good boy who has been celebrated in song by Lemuel F. Parton, the New York newspaperman:

> I have led a good life, full of peace and quiet,
> I shall have an old age, full of rum and riot;
> I have been a good boy, wed to peace and study,
> I shall have an old age, ribald, coarse and bloody.

> I have never cut throats, even when I yearned to,
> Never sang the dirty songs that my fancy turned to;
> I have been a nice boy and done what was expected,
> I shall be an old bum loved but unrespected.

FRANK SHAY

Provincetown, Mass.
June 1, 1928

Acknowledgments

It is a great pleasure to acknowledge the expert and valuable assistance given me by Judge Louis B. Hart, of Buffalo, Mr. W. W. Dean, of Indianapolis and others. Thanks are also due to Mr. Cardwell Thomson, H. Douglas Hadden, Robert Edwards, William B. Smith, John Held, Jr., D'Arcy Dahlberg, Miss Margaret Marshall, Harry T. Ramsey, Collins B. Reed, Mr. and Mrs. Edward J. (Tex) O'Reilly, James O'Reilly and Hal S. White.

The thanks of Miss Ramsey and myself must go to Cyril Mockridge for his patience and consideration.

Mr. Held's graphic illustrations again are used through the courtesy of *The New Yorker* and the Weyhe Galleries.

"JUST BREAK THE NEWS TO MOTHER"

EARLY AMERICAN FOLK SONG   ENG.BY JOHN HELD JR

More Pious Friends and Drunken Companions

THE FATAL CARD

A Pack of Cards

As sung by John Held, Jr.

One night as I sat by my fire-side so wea-ry, And dream-ing of friends who were far, far a-way; My mem-o-ry brought me some that's sad and drear-y, Yet oth-ers came, too, that were cheer-ful and gay. When all of a sud-den I found my eyes rest-ing On some-thing that brought man-y scenes to my

mind, 'Twas an   old pack of cards, and some tales in - ter -

est - ing,   I   thought   that   I   might   in   their

his - to - ry   find!   The   first scene that   I

saw that night,   I thought was quite a   pleas-ant sight, A

grand old room a - blaze with light,   I whis-pered "kind   re -

gards." Whilst round the board sat young and   old,   They

played for love and   not for gold, Whilst joy and sor-row

all un - told, was   in that deck   of   cards!

The next scene I saw filled my heart with great pity,
It was a young man and his parents I knew,
'Twas their only son whom they'd sent to the city
To study and grow up a gentleman true,
A weekly allowance they thought would suffice him,
To live on the best and for studies to pay,
They knew not that evil companions enticed him
Away from his studies at poker to play!

       I saw him as he left his seat,
       He never thought his pals would cheat,
       Each time he played he met defeat,
       And still he called them pards.
       But there will come a reckoning day,
       And he will through this foolish play
       Bring sorrow in the old folks' way,
       All through that pack of cards!

The last scene of all I beheld with much sorrow,
For there was the scene of the gambler's black fate,
No thought had they got of the waking tomorrow
Though then they'd repent but to find it too late.
The bright gold was stacked by the side of each player,
The miser's black greed was in every man's heart,
As quickly the bets passed twixt backer and layer,
And Ruin was King in the Devil's slave mart!

       "I'll stake a hundred on this game!"
       "I'll go you, sir, I'll do the same."
       Who cares for misery and shame,
       As each his treasure guards?
       "You lie! I saw you turn that ace,"
       A smashing blow right in the face;
       A pistol shot, and death's disgrace,
       Was in that pack of cards!

The Roving Gambler

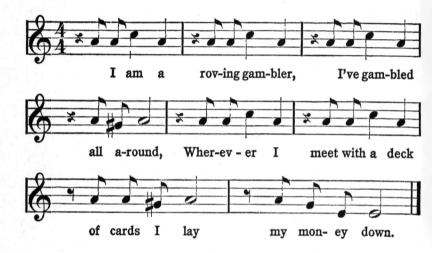

I am a rov-ing gam-bler, I've gam-bled all a-round, Wher-ev - er I meet with a deck of cards I lay my mon- ey down.

I've gambled down in Washington and I've gambled over in Spain;
I am on my way to Georgia to knock down my last game.

I had not been in Washington many more weeks than three,
Till I fell in love with a pretty little girl and she fell in love with me.

She took me in her parlor, she cooled me with her fan,
She whispered low in her mother's ears, "I love this gambling man."

"Oh daughter, Oh dear daughter, how could you treat me so,
To leave your dear old mother and with a gambler go?"

"Oh mother, Oh dear mother, you know I love you well,
But the love I hold for this gambling man no human tongue can tell.

"I wouldn't marry a farmer, for he's always in the rain;
The man I want is a gambling man who wears the big gold chain.

"I wouldn't marry a blacksmith, for he's always in the dirt;
For the man I want is the gambling man who wears a ruffled shirt.

"I wouldn't marry a doctor, for he is always gone from home;
All I want is the gambling man, for he won't leave me alone.

"I wouldn't marry a railroad man, and this is the reason why:
I never saw a railroad man that wouldn't tell his wife a lie.

"I hear the train a-coming, she's coming 'round the curve,
Whistling and a-blowing and straining every nerve.

"Oh mother, oh dear mother, I'll tell you if I can;
If you ever see me coming back again I'll be with the gambling man."

"I've gambled down in Washington and I've gambled over in Spain;
I am on my way to Georgia to knock down my last game."

Australian Highwayman's Song

As sung by Margaret Marshall

Once a jol - ly swag-man camped be-side a bil - ly bong,

Un - der the shade of a ku - li - bar tree, and he

sang as he sat and wait - ed for his bil - ly - boil,

You'll come a - waltz - ing Ma - til - da with me.

Chorus

Waltz - ing Ma - til - da, waltz - ing Ma-til - da,

You'll come waltz-ing Ma - til - da with me, And he

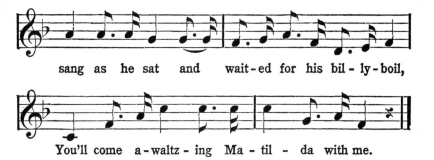

sang as he sat   and   wait - ed for his bil - ly - boil,

You'll come a - waltz - ing Ma - til - da with me.

Down came a jumbok to drink at the billy-bong,
Up jumped the swag-man and shot it with glee,
And he sang as he stuffed that jumbok in his tucker-bag,
"You'll come a-waltzing Matilda with me."

Chorus :

Waltzing Matilda, waltzing Matilda,
You'll come waltzing Matilda with me,
And he sang as he stuffed that jumbok in his tucker-bag,
"You'll come a-waltzing Matilda with me."

Up rode the stockman mounted on his thoroughbred,
Up rode the troopers, one, two, three,
"Where is the jumbok you have in your tucker-bag?
"You'll come a-waltzing Matilda with me."

Chorus :

Waltzing Matilda, waltzing Matilda,
You'll come waltzing Matilda with me,
"Where is the jumbok you have in your tucker-bag?
You'll come a-waltzing Matilda with me."

Up jumped the swag-man, leaped into the billy-bong,
"You'll never catch me alive," said he.

(Slowly)

And his ghost may be heard as you pass by the billy-bong,

(Fast)

"You'll come a-waltzing Matilda with me."

Chorus :

Waltzing Matilda, waltzing Matilda,

You'll come waltzing Matilda with me,

(Slowly)

And his ghost may be heard as you pass by the billy-bong,

(Fast)

"You'll come a-waltzing Matilda with me,

GLOSSARY

Swagman, highwayman. Billy-bong, brook. Billy-boil, coffee.
Jumbok, lamb.

Our Gude-Man

Our gude-man cam' hame at e'en,
   And hame cam' he;
And there he saw a saddle-horse,
   Whaur nae horse should be.
"Oh, how cam' this horse here,
   How can this be?
How cam' this horse here,
   Without the leave of me?"
     "A horse?" quo' she,
     "Ay, a horse," quo' he.
"Ye auld blind doited carle,
   Blinder mat ye be!
'Tis naething but a milk-cow
   My minnie sent to me."
     "A milk-cow!" quo' he,
     "Ay, a milk-cow," quo' she.

"Far ha'e I ridden,
 And meikle ha'e I seen;
But a saddle on a cow's back
 Saw I never nane!"

Our gude-man cam' hame at e'en,
 And hame cam' he;
He spied a pair o' jack-boots,
 Whaur nae boots should be.
"What's this now, gude-wife?
 What's this I see?
How cam' these boots here,
 Without the leave o' me?"
  "Boots?" quo' she,
  "Ay, boots," quo' he.
"Shame fa' your cuckold face,
 And ill mat ye see!
It's but a pair o' water-stoups
 The cooper sent to me."
  "Water-stoups!" quo' he.
  "Ay, water-stoups," quo' she.
"Far ha'e I ridden,
 And farer ha'e I gane;
But siller spurs on water stoups
 Saw I never nane!"

Our gude-man cam' hame at e'en,
 And hame cam' he;
And there he saw a sword,
 Whaur nae sword should be.
"What's this now, gude-wife?
 What's this I see?
Oh, how cam' this sword here,
 Without the leave o' me?"
  "A sword?" quo' she.
  "Ay, a sword," quo' he.
"Shame fa' your cuckold face,

And ill mat ye see!
It's but a parritch spurtle
  My minnie sent to me.
    "A spurtle?" quo' he.
    "Ay, a spurtle," quo' she.
"Weel far ha'e I ridden,
  And meikle ha'e I seen;
But silver-handled spurtles
  Saw I never nane!"

Our gude-man cam' hame at e'en,
  And hame cam' he;
There he spied a pouthered wig,
  Whaur nae wig should be.
"What's this now, gude-wife?
  What's this I see?
How cam' this wig here,
  Without the leave o' me?"
    "A wig?" quo' she.
    "Ay, a wig," quo' he.
"Shame fa' your cuckold face,
  And ill mat ye see!
'Tis naething but a clockin' hen
  My minnie sent to me.
    "A clockin' hen?" quo' he.
    "Ay, a clockin' hen," quo' she.
"Far ha'e I ridden,
  And meikle ha'e I seen;
But pouther on a clockin' hen
  Saw I never nane!"

Our gude-man cam' hame at e'en,
  And hame cam' he;
And there he saw a riding-coat,
  Whaur nae coat shoud be.
"Oh, how cam' this coat here?
  How can this be?

How cam' this coat here,
  Without the leave o' me?"
    "A coat?" quo' she.
    "Ay, a coat," quo' he.
"Ye auld blind dotard carle,
  Blinder mat ye be!
It's but a pair o' blankets
  My minnie sent to me."
    "Blankets?" quo' he.
    "Aye, blankets," quo' she.
"Far ha'e I ridden,
  And meikle ha'e I seen;
But buttons upon blankets
  Saw I never nane!"

Bed went our gude-man.
  And bed went he;
And there he spied a sturdy man,
  Whaur nae man should be.
"How cam' this man here?
  How can this be?
How cam' this man here,
  Without the leave o' me?"
    "A man?" quo' she.
    "Ay, a doited man," quo' he.
"Puir blind body!
  And blinder mat ye be!
It's a new milking-maid
  My minnie sent to me."
    "A maid?" quo' he.
    "Ay, a maid," quo' she.
"Far ha'e I ridden
  And meikle ha'e I seen;
But lang-bearded milking-maids
  Saw I never nane!"

Down in Dear Old Greenwich Village

As sung by Bobby Edwards

The only example of folk-song building to come to the editor's immediate attention is the following national anthem of New York's bohemia. Back in the old days when the Village began and ended at Polly's, when certain now distinguished men and women of letters were known as Oney, Theo, Jig, Sue and Vincent; when other names that are now known across the continent were just so many boys and girls struggling for recognition while living in garrets and basements and the editor had a beautiful hall-bedroom overlooking Washington Square for two dollars a week, the following ballad had its beginnings. Bobby Edwards, the last of the troubadours, gave it a prominent place in his repertory and later put it on paper. It is now so much his that the fullest credit must be given him. Nevertheless it is an indubitable folk-ballad in its origin and the first I ever heard sing it was George Baker, one evening at the aforesaid Polly's.

Allegro con inchistro rosso

Way down South in Green-wich Vil-lage that's the field for cul-ture's til-lage; there they have ar - tis - tic rav-ings,

tea and oth - er aw - ful crav-ings: but there the in-spir-

a - tion stops And they start sil - ly lit - tle shops You'll

find them an - y - where 'round Wash-ing-ton Square.

Down in dear old Greenwich Village,
 There they wear no fancy frillage,
For the ladies of the square
 All wear smocks and bob their hair.
There they do not think it shocking
 To wear stencils for a stocking,
That saves the laundry bills
 In Washington Square.

Way down South in Greenwich Village,
 Where the spinsters come for thrillage,

There they speak of "sex relations,"
  With the sordid Slavic nations.
'Neath the guise of feminism,
  Dodging social ostracism,
They get away with much
  In Washington Square.

Way down South in Greenwich Village,
  Where they all consume distillage,
Where the fashion illustrators
  Flirt with interior decorators.
There the cheap Bohemian fakirs
  And the boys from Wanamaker's
Gather "atmosphere"
  In Washington Square.

Way down South in Greenwich Village,
  Where the brains amount to nillage,
Where the girls are unconventional,
  And the men are unintentional.
There the girls are self-supporting,
  There the ladies do the courting,
The ladies buy the "eats"
  In Washington Square.

Way down South in Greenwich Village,
  Comes a bunch of Uptown Swillage,
Folks from Lenox Subway Stations
  Come with lurid expectations.
There the Village informalities
  Are construed as abnormalities
By the boobs that visit Sheridan Square.

The Wreck of the Old 97

They give him his orders at Monroe, Virginia,
Saying, "Pete, you are away behind time;
This is not Thirty-eight, but it's old Ninety-seven,
You must put her in Center on time."

He looked around and says to his black greasy fireman,
"Just shovel in a little more coal:
And when we cross that White Oak Mountain,
You can watch old Ninety-seven roll."

It's a mighty rough road from Lynchburg to Danville
And a line on a three-mile grade;
It was on that grade he lost his average,
And you see what a jump he made.

He was going down-grade making ninety miles an hour,
When his whistle broke into a scream.
He was found in the wreck with his hand on the throttle
And was scalded to death with the steam.

Now, ladies, you must take warning
From this time now on:
Never speak harsh words to your true love and husband
He may leave you and never return.

The Female Smuggler

Now, in sailor's clothing swell Jane did go,
Dressed like a sailor from top to toe;
Her aged father was the only care
Of this female smuggler,
      Of this female smuggler
      Who never did despair.

With her pistols loaded she went aboard.
And by her side hung a glittering sword,
In her belt two daggers; well armed for war
Was this female smuggler,
      Was this female smuggler,
      Who never feared a scar.

Now they had not sail-ed far from the land,
When a strange sail brought them to a stand.
"These are sea robbers," this maid did cry,
"But the female smuggler,
      But the female smuggler,
      Will conquer or will die."

Alongside, then, this strange vessel came.
"Cheer up," cried Jane, "we will board the same;
We'll run all chances to rise or fall,"
Cried this female smuggler,
      Cried this female smuggler,
      Who never feared a ball.

Now they killed those pirates and took their store,
And soon returned to Old England's shore.
With a keg of brandy she walked along,
Did this female smuggler,
      Did this female smuggler,
      Who sweetly sang a song.

Now they were followed by the blockade,
Who in irons strong did put this young maid.
But when they brought her to be tried,
This young female smuggler,
     This young female smuggler
     Stood dressed like a bride.

Their commodore against her appeared,
And for her life she greatly feared.
When he did find to his great surprise
'Twas a female smuggler,
     'Twas a female smuggler
     Had fought him in disguise.

He to the judge and jury said,
"I cannot prosecute this maid,
Pardon for her on my knees I crave,
For this female smuggler,
     For this female smuggler
     So valiant and so brave."

Then this commodore to her father went,
To gain her hand he asked his consent.
His consent he gained, so the commodore
And the female smuggler,
     And the female smuggler
     Are one for evermore.

O, Give Me a Home Where the Buffalo Roam

As sung by Harry T. Ramsey

Oh, give me a home Where the buf - fa - lo
roam, Where the deer and the an - te - lope play Where
sel - dom is heard A dis - cour - ag - ing
word, And the sky is not cloud - ed all day.

Chorus

A ho - me, A ho - me where the
deer and the an - te - lope play, Where

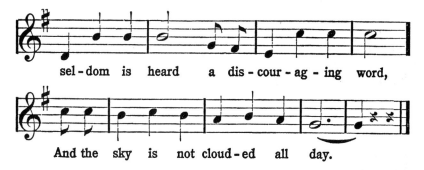

sel-dom is heard a dis-cour-ag-ing word,

And the sky is not cloud-ed all day.

O, give me a gale on the Solomon vale,
  Where life's stream joyfully flows,
On the banks of the Beaver where seldom, if ever,
  Any poisonous herbage doth grow.

Chorus

O, give me a land where the bright diamond sand
  Lies by the glittering stream,
Where glideth along, the graceful white Swan,
  Like a maid in her heavenly dream.

Chorus

Ofttimes at night, when summers are bright,
  By the light of twinkling stars,
I've stood here amazed, and asked as I gazed,
  If their glory exceeds that of ours.

Chorus

Heenan and Sayers

It was on the sixteenth day of April that they agreed to fight,
The money was all put up and everything was right,
But Heenan was arrested and brought to the county jail,
Where he was held to keep the peace under three hundred bail.

His friends went quickly there and they did bail him out,
He was forced to change his training ground and take another route;
They thought for to discourage him, so as to prevent the mill,
But having a brave heart in him, swore that Sayers' blood he'd spill.

To see those heroes in the ring it would make your heart feel gay,
Each wore a smile upon his face in honor of the day:
The spectators say they were eager those champions for to see,
For they both said that they'd either die or gain the victory.

Time was called, they both stood up, the excitement it was great,
To see those champions seeking to seal each other's fate;
Sayers he made a left-hand punch at Heenan's pretty face,
Who quickly dodged and with a blow laid Tommy near a case.

But when the second round came on the Briton was up to time,
Heenan made a pass at him, which slightly bruised his dial;
His friends they began to cheer, which made Sayers feel sad,
For he thought that he'd easily win, which would make the Yankees mad.

Sayers was up to time again, and his face it bore a smile.
Heenan made a pass at him, which slightly bruised his dial;
He made a terrific right-hand punch, which got on Heenan's jowl,
But quickly a sledge-hammer blow caused Sayers for to howl.

A look of melancholy was upon each Briton's face;
They thought that Sayers would get whipped and to England be a
    disgrace;

But then he got a handsome blow on brave Heenan's nob,
Their faces bore a smile again, and the betting on Sayers was odd.

Time was called, they both were up to toe the scratch once more,
Sayers got home on Heenan's mug, which made the Britons roar;
Heenan followed quickly up, and as Sayers turned around,
He met him with a right-hand blow which sprawled him on the ground.

Bold Sayers was up to time again, and he looked very bad;
Heenan looked as fresh again, which made the Britons mad;
They had a little false sparring, then at each other did gaze,
When Heenan sprawled him out again, which did the bulls amaze.

Then the cheers and bawls of Heenan's friends would make your heart
    feel gay;
For they were sure, they had no doubt, but he would gain the day:
The friends of Sayers began to think that he would soon give in,
And to think their champion would get beat it caused them to grin.

The fight was drawing to a close, the excitement growing worse,
The friends of Heenan they did cheer, and of Sayers they did curse,
The bulls were sure that Heenan would win, which caused them all to
    fret,
For every cent that they were worth on Sayers it was bet.

But then the thirty-seventh round came on to be the last,
The Briton's friends they plainly saw their man was failing fast;
When Heenan gave him another blow, which made them feel forlorn—
The Briton's friends jumped in the ring and said the fight was drawn.

But Heenan called on Sayers again to come and fight it out,
But he was so badly punished he could scarcely open his mouth:
Heenan said: "The fight is mine—and stood upon his ground—
Saying: "I am the champion of the world, in the thirty-seventh round."

Rio Grande

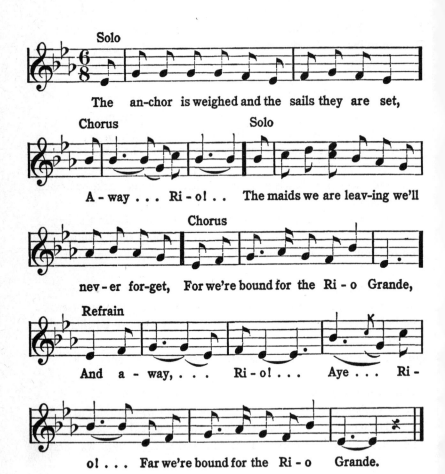

The an-chor is weighed and the sails they are set,

A - way . . . Ri - o! . . The maids we are leav-ing we'll

nev - er for-get, For we're bound for the Ri - o Grande,

And a - way, . . . Ri - o! . . . Aye . . . Ri -

o! . . . Far we're bound for the Ri - o Grande.

So it's pack up your donkey and get under way,
     Away, Rio!
The girls we are leaving can take half our pay,

Chorus

We'll sing as we heave to the maidens we leave
    Away, Rio!
And you who are listening, good-bye to you,

       Chorus

Come heave up the anchor, let's get it aweigh
    Away, Rio!
It's got a firm hold, so heave steady, I say,

       Chorus

False Henry

Just a year ago tonight, mother, how sorrowful were we,
When sister May was taken, upon her wedding day;
O, mother, dearest mother, how much better it would have been for me,
Could I have died just like her, in my innocence and glee.

Just a year ago tonight, mother, I went down to a ball,
I went with my dear Henry, and danced with him till dawn;
There was not another maiden, with a lighter heart than mine,
But tonight I lie here dying, a mother, but no wife.

There will be a dance tonight, mother, and crowded it will be,
And I know that he will be with them, and he will think of me;
I own I love dear Henry, much better than I do life,
But tonight I lay here dying, a mother, but no wife.

Take this ring from off my finger, where he placed it long ago,
Give it to him with a blessing, and in joy let him go;
Just tell him I'll forgive him, for my sorrow and his sin;
Raise the curtains higher, dear mother, for my eyes are growing dim.

Here is my baby boy, mother, take and raise him up for me,
And give him food and plenty as you always did for me;
Then goodby, mother dearest, and you, my baby boy,
And you, my false young Henry, and she bade her last farewell.

The Charming Young Widow I Met on the Train

I live in Ver - mont, and one morn-ing last sum - mer, A let - ter in - form'd me my un - cle was dead; And al - so re - quest-ed I'd come down to Bos - ton, As he'd left me a large sum of mon - ey it said. Of course I de-termin'd on mak - ing the jour - ney, And to book my - self

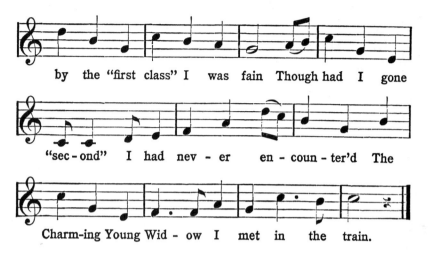

by the "first class" I was fain Though had I gone

"sec - ond" I had nev - er en - coun - ter'd The

Charm-ing Young Wid - ow I met in the train.

Now scarce was I seated within the compartment
Before a fresh passenger entered the door:
'Twas a female, a young one, and dressed in deep mourning,
An infant in long clothes she gracefully bore.
A white cap surrounded a face, oh, so lovely!
I never shall look on one like it again.
I fell deep in love over-head in a moment
With the charming young widow I met on the train.

The widow and I side by side sat together,
The carriage containing ourselves and no more;
When the silence was broken by my fair companion,
Who enquired the time by the watch that I wore.
I, of course, satisfied her, and then conversation
Was freely indulged in by both, till my brain
Fairly reeled with excitement, I grew so enchanted
With the charming young widow I met on the train.

We became so familiar I ventured to ask
How old was the child she held at her breast.
"Ah, sir," she responded, and into tears bursting,
Her infant, still closer, convulsively pressed.

"When I think of my child, I am well nigh distracted,
Its father, my husband, my heart breaks with pain."
She, choking with sobs, laid her head on my waistcoat,
Did the charming young widow I met on the train.

By this time the train arrived at a station
Within a few miles of the great one in town.
When my charmer exclaimed, as she looked through the window:
"Good gracious alive! Why there goes Mr. Brown.
He's my late husband's brother—dear sir, would you kindly
My best-beloved child for a moment sustain?"
Of course I complied, then off to the platform
Tripped the charming young widow I met on the train.

Three minutes elapsed, when the whistle it sounded,
The train began moving; no widow appeared.
I bawled out, "Stop! Stop!" But they paid no attention.
With a snort and a jerk starting off as I feared.
In this horrid dilemma I sought for the hour.
But my watch—oh, where was it? And where was my chain?
My purse, too, my ticket, my gold pencil case? All gone!
Oh, that artful young widow I met on the train.

While I was my loss so deeply bewailing
The train again stopped and I "Tickets, please," heard.
So I told the conductor, while dandling the infant,
The loss I'd sustained, but he doubted my word.
He called more officials, a lot gathered 'round me,
Uncovered the child—oh, how shall I explain?
For behold, 'twas no baby, 'twas only a dummy.
Oh, the crafty young widow I met on the train!

Satisfied I'd been robbed, they allowed my departure,
Though, of course, I'd settle my fare the next day;
And now I wish to counsel young men from the country
Lest they should get served in a similar way.

Beware of young widows you meet on the railway,
Who lean on your shoulder, whose tears fall like rain;
Look out for your pocket—in case they resemble
The charming young widow I met on the train.

Hop Head

As sung by Judith Tobey

Hop Head went for a dreamy stroll,
    Looking for a pill that he couldn't roll.
Roasted and toasted the whole night through,
    Till he dangled at the end of a chink's bamboo.

Dreamt he had a million nickels and dimes,
    Counted 'em over a million times.
Million girls so pretty and fair,
    With big blue eyes and golden hair.

Went to England to get away from jails,
    There he got acquainted with the Prince of Wales.
Took his watch and his diamond pin—
    And along came a Bobby and run him in.

Went to China for to fight Japan,
    There he got acquainted with Li Hung Chan,
Li Hung Chan said, "Perhaps—
    You'd be better off in Brooklyn shootin' craps."

So he laid his head on a Suey Pow,
And stabbed himself with a Yen Shi Gow,
And in the morning won't you let me in,
    'Cause Hop Sing Toy you're a friend of mine.

Salvation Army Song

As sung by Helen Ramsey

There was a man in our town, I think his name was

Brown; He prayed for Pro - hi - bi - tion but he

vot - ed for R - U - M. He helped to put the

poi - son in his neigh-bor's C - U - P; And

now he laughs at us be-cause we're S - A - V - E - D.

Chorus :

Oh G-L-O-R-Y, we are S-A-V-E-D,
H-A-P-P-Y to be F-R-double EE,
Oh V-I-C-T-O-R-Y from the bonds of S-I-N
Glory, glory, Hallelujah, Tra-la-la, Amen.

Some people go on week days
To D-A-N-C-E
They go to church on Sundays
To show their H-A-T.
Some people daub their faces up
With P-A-I-N-T
And then they laugh at us
Because we're S-A-V-E-D.

Chorus

I love to stand on the corner
With my D-R-U-M, drum
It brings to us the sinner
And the B-U-M, bum, bum
They come to us from hovel
And from D-I-T-C-H
And we march on to Victory
Without H-I-T-C-H.

Hannah

I've got a girl named Hannah,
From Butte, Montana.
The reason I don't love her,
She's dead, gol darn her!

She lived on the
Untrodden hills of Butte.
None cared to love her
And none dared to shoot!

The Cannibal Maiden

As sung by Collins B. Reed

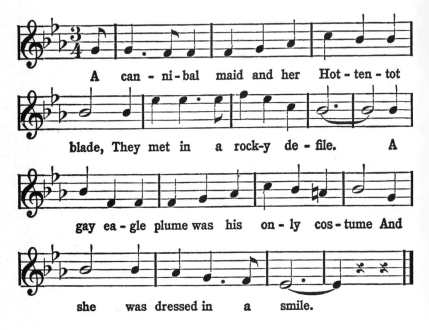

A can - ni - bal maid and her Hot - ten - tot blade, They met in a rock - y de - file. A gay ea - gle plume was his on - ly cos - tume And she was dressed in a smile.

Together they strolled as his passions he told
   In thrilling and tremulous mien,
She had murmured the word when a war whoop was heard,
   And a rival burst out on the scene.

'Twas a savage Zulu to the trysting place drew
   Demanding his cannibal bride,
But the Hottentot said, with a toss of his head,
   "I'll have thy degenerate hide!"

So the Hottentot flew at the savage Zulu
   And the Zulu he flew at the blade;
Together they vied in their strength and their pride
   As they fought for the cannibal maid.

She perched on a stone with her shapely shin bone
  Clasped in her long twining arms,
And watched the blood fly with a love-laden eye
  As the warriors fought for her charms.

Oh, the purple blood flows from the Hottentot's nose,
  And the Zulu is struck by the blade,
As together they vied in their strength and their pride,
  And they died for the cannibal maid.

She made a fine stew of the savage Zulu
  And she scrambled the Hottentot's brains;
'Twas a dainty menu when the cooking was thru
  And she dined from her lovers' remains.

Oh, the savage Zulu and the Hottentot too
  Are asleep in a cannibal tomb;
The three are made one—my story is done,
  And the maiden walked off in the gloom.

Life Is But a Game of Cards

Life is but a game of cards, which each one has to learn:
Each shuffles, cuts and deals a pack, and each a trump does turn:
Some turn a high card at the top, while others turn a low;
Some hold a hand quite full of trumps, while others none can show.

Some shuffle with a practiced hand and pack their cards with care,
So they may know when they are dealt where all the leaders are;
Thus fools are made the dupe of rogue and rogues each other cheat;
But he is very wise, indeed, who never meets defeat.

In playing some will lead the ace, their counting card to save.
Some play the deuce, and some the trey, and many play the knave.
Some play for money, and some for fun, and some for worldly fame.
And not until the game's played out can they count up the gain.

When hearts are trumps some play for love, then pleasure decks the
    hour.
No thought of sorrow checks our joy in rosy, beauteous bower.
We dance and sing, sweet music make, our cards at random play,
And while the heart remains on top our game is but a holiday.

When diamonds chance to crown the top, then players stake their gold;
And heavy sums are won and lost by gamblers young and old;
Intent on winning, each doth watch his cards with eager eye,
So he may watch his neighbor's hand and cheat him on the sly.

When clubs are trumps, look out for war, on ocean and on land,
For bloody deeds are often done when clubs are in the hand;
Then lives are staked instead of gold, the days are wornout breed,
Across the broad Atlantic now, see clubs have got the lead.

And last of all is when the spade is turned by hand of Time,
And always finishes up the game in every land and clime;
No matter how much a man may win, or how much a man may save,
You'll find the spade turns up at last and digs the player's grave.

Pictures from Life's Other Side

Sung by Hal S. White

Fragment

The next scene was that of a gambler
Who gambled his money away;
Stole a ring from his dead mother's finger
That she wore on her wedding day.
That night he went out on the highway,
"Hands up! Money or your life," he cried.
Then he took with his knife
His own brother's life:
       That's a picture from life's other side!

Old Joe Clark

I don't like Old Joe Clark,
    Don't think I ever shall.
I don't like Old Joe Clark,
    Always liked his girl.

        Rock, rock, rock, Old Joe Clark
           Good-bye, Betsy Brown.
        Rock, rock, rock, Old Joe Clark
           Goin' to leave this town.

Oh, if I had a needle and thread
    As fine as I could sew;
I'd sew myself to Joe Clark's bride
    And down the road we'd go.

        Walk, walk, walk, Old Joe Clark,
           Good-bye, Betsy Brown.
        Walk, walk, walk, Old Joe Clark,
           Say good-bye to your Betsy Brown.

.   .   .   .   .

John Brown's wife takes whiskey in her tea,
John Brown's wife takes whiskey in her tea,
John Brown's wife takes whiskey in her tea,
    As we go rolling home,

        Glory, glory, hallelujah!
        Glory, glory, hallelujah!
        Glory, glory, hallelujah!
        As we go rolling home.

.   .   .   .   .

She was an old hen and she had a wooden foot,
    And she made her nest near a huckleberry root;
She laid more eggs than any hen on the farm
    And another little drink wouldn't do us any harm.

Cocaine Bill and Morphine Sue

As sung by Mary Jacobsen

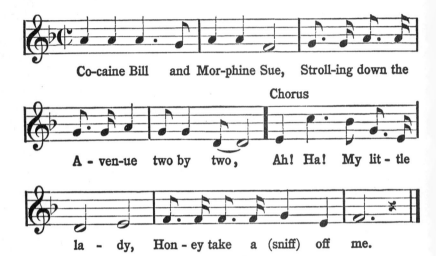

Co-caine Bill and Mor-phine Sue, Stroll-ing down the

Chorus

A - ven-ue two by two, Ah! Ha! My lit - tle

la - dy, Hon - ey take a (sniff) off me.

They walked down the East Side full of hope,
Until they saw a sign reading—"No More Dope."

Chorus

Said Bill to Sue, "This will never do,
We gotta get a shot and it's up to you."

Chorus

Sue loved the men and she knew her stuff,
She walked into a drug store prepared to treat 'em rough.

Chorus

She rolled her eyes and she cocked her head
She said, "Come here I want some dope and I won't be misled."

Chorus

She got what she wanted but her tale is sad
Her stuff was good, but the dope was bad.

Chorus

Bill he sighed, and Sue she cried,
And then they both lay down and died.

Chorus

Now in the graveyard side by side
Lie Cocaine Bill and his Morphine bride.

Rollicking Bill the Sailor

This bit must be meat and drink to those initiates who know the correct words. There are many versions, all of them far better than the appended sample, but it is well to remember that the Pilgrims landed on the rock.

"Who's that a-knocking at my door?"
    Cried the fair young maiden.
"Who's that a-knocking at my door?"
    Cried the fair young maiden.

"It's me, myself, and nobody else!"
    Cried Rollicking Bill, the Sailor.
"It's me, myself, and nobody else!"
    Cried Rollicking Bill, the Sailor.

"But we have only one bed!"
    Cried the fair young maiden.
"But we have only one bed!"
    Cried the fair young maiden.

Well, figure it out for yourself and damned be he who first cries, " Hold ! Enough !"

Texas Rangers

Come, all you Texas rangers, wherever you may be,
I'll tell you of some troubles that happened unto me.
My name is nothing extra, so it I will not tell,—
And here's to all you rangers, I am sure I wish you well.

It was at the age of sixteen that I joined the jolly band,
We marched from San Antonio down to the Rio Grande.
Our captain he informed us, perhaps he thought it right,
"Before we reach the station, boys, you'll surely have to fight."

And when the bugle sounded our captain gave command,
"To arms, to arms," he shouted, "and by your horses stand."
I saw the smoke ascending, it seemed to reach the sky;
The first thought that struck me, my time had come to die.

I saw the Indians coming, I heard them give the yell;
My feelings at that moment, no tongue can ever tell.
I saw the glittering lances, their arrows round me flew,
And all my strength it left me and all my courage too.

We fought full nine hours before the strife was o'er,
The like of dead and wounded I never saw before.
And when the sun was rising and the Indians they had fled,
We loaded up our rifles and counted up our dead.

All of us were wounded, our noble captain slain,
And the sun was shining sadly across the bloody plain.
Sixteen as brave rangers as ever roamed the West
Were buried by their comrades with arrows in their breast.

'Twas then I thought of mother, who to me in tears did say,
"To you they are all strangers, with me you had better stay."
I thought that she was childish, the best she did not know;
My mind was fixed on ranging and I was bound to go.

Perhaps you have a mother, likewise a sister too,
And maybe you have a sweetheart to weep and mourn for you;
If that be your situation, although you'd like to roam,
I'll advise you by experience, you had better stay at home.

I have seen the fruits of rambling, I know its hardships well;
I have crossed the Rocky Mountains, rode down the streets of hell;
I have been in the great southwest where the wild Apaches roam,
And I tell you from experience you had better stay at home.

And now my song is ended; I guess I have sung enough;
The life of a ranger I am sure is very tough.
And here's to all you ladies, I am sure I wish you well,
I am bound to go a-ranging, so ladies, fare you well.

Cocaine Lil and Morphine Sue

Did you ever hear about Cocaine Lil?
She lived in Cocaine town on Cocaine hill,
She had a cocaine dog and a cocaine cat,
They fought all night with a cocaine rat.

She had cocaine hair on her cocaine head.
She had a cocaine dress that was poppy red;
She wore a snowbird hat and sleigh-riding clothes.
On her coat she wore a crimson, cocaine rose.

Big gold chariots on the Milky Way,
Snakes and elephants silver and gray.
Oh the cocaine blues they make me sad,
Oh the cocaine blues make me feel bad.

Lil went to a snow party one cold night,
And the way she sniffed was sure a fright.
There was Hophead Mag with Dopey Slim
Kankakee Liz and Yen Shee Jim.

There was Morphine Sue and the Poppy Face Kid,
Climbed up snow ladders and down they skid;
There was the Stepladder Kit, a good six feet,
And the Sleigh-riding Sister who were hard to beat.

Along in the morning about half past three
They were all lit up like a Christmas tree;
Lil got home and started for bed,
Took another sniff and it knocked her dead.

They laid her out in her cocaine clothes:
She wore a snowbird hat with a crimson rose;
On her headstone you'll find this refrain:
"She died as she lived, sniffing cocaine."

Oh, No, John!

As sung by the Fuller Sisters

On yonder hill there stands a creature,
    Who she is I do not know;
I'll go and court her for her beauty,
    She must answer "Yes" or "No."
Oh, no, John, no, John, no, John, no.

My father was a Spanish captain,
    Went to sea a month ago;
First he kissed me, then he left me,
    Bade me always answer "No!"
Oh, no, John, no, John, no, John, no.

O madam, in your face is beauty,
    On your lips red roses grow;
Will you take me for your lover?
    Madam, answer "Yes" or "No."
Oh, no, John, no, John, no, John, no.

O madam, I will give you jewels,
  I will make you rich and free,
I will give you silken dresses;
  Madam, will you marry me?
Oh, no, John, no, John, no, John, no.

O madam, if you are so cruel,
  And that you do scorn me so,
If I may not be your lover,
  Madam, will you let me go?
Oh, no, John, no, John, no, John, no.

Then I will stay with you forever,
  Since you will not be unkind;
Madam, I have vowed to love you,
  Would you have me change my mind?
Oh, no, John, no, John, no, John, no.

Hark! I hear the trumpets ringing,
  Will you come and be my wife?
Or, dear madam, have you settled
  To live single all your life?
Oh, no, John, no, John, no, John, no.

Duckfoot Sue

    For now I'll sing to you
    Of the girl I love so true;
She's chief engineer of the night shirt line,
    And her name is Duckfoot Sue.
    Her beauty is all she has;
    She's a mouth as big as a crab;
She has an upper lip like the rudder of a ship,
    And I'll tell you she is mad.

Willie the Weeper

Did you ev - er hear tell a-bout Wil-lie the weep - er,

Wil-lie the weep - er was a chim - ney sweep - er,

Had the dope hab - it and had it bad,

Lis - ten while I'll tell you 'bout the dream he had.

He went to a hop house on Sat'day night,
　'Cause he knew the lights would be burning bright.
Then he smoked a dozen pills or more,
　Dreamt he was living on a foreign shore.

Around a lay-out table a couple of hop-fiends lay,
　Come closer and I'll tell you what they had to say,
Tales of money they were going to make
　And faro banks they were goin' to break.

He went to Monte Carlo and he played roulette,
　He couldn't lose a dollar, won every single bet.
Then they told him that the bank was broke,
　He bought eighteen million dollars worth of coke.

This is the tale of Willie the Weeper,
   Willie the Weeper who was a chimney sweeper,
Went to sleep on his hall-room flop,
   Dreamt he had a million dollars worth of hop.

Hop Song

As Reported by Judge Louis B. Hart

Rich people now they don't take a drop,
   They fill themselves up on cocaine or the hop.
Singing: Oh! Oh! Honey! Baby, won't you be mine?
         Have a (sniff) on me!

Walked up Broadway down on Main,
   Tried to dig up a dime to buy some cocaine.
Singing: Oh! Oh! Honey! Baby, won't you be mine?
         Have a (sniff) on me!

Cocaine's for horses and it's not for men,
   Doctor says 'twill kill you, but don't say when.
Singing: Oh! Oh! Honey! Baby, won't you be mine?
         Have a (sniff) on me!

When I die bury me low,
   Bury me deep in a nice bunch of snow.
Singing: Oh! Oh! Honey! Baby, won't you be mine?
         Have a (sniff) on me!

*On the (sniff) the gesture of closing a nostril with one finger and tapping
the base of the other with another.*

Johnny Sands

As sung by Harry T. Ramsey

There was a man named John-ny Sands who mar-ried Bet-ty Hague, And though she brought him gold and lands She proved a ter-ri-ble plague. For, oh, she was a scold-ing wife, full of ca-price and whim, He said that he was tired of life and she was tired of him, And she was tired of him.

Said he, "My dear, I'll drown myself,
The river runs below."
Said she, "Pray do, you silly elf,
I've wished it long ago."
Says he, "Upon the brink I'll stand.
Do you run down the hill
And push me in with all your might."
Says she, "My dear, I will."
Says she, "My dear, I will."

"For fear that I should courage lack
And try to save my life,
Pray tie my hands behind my back."
"I will," replied his wife.
She tied them fast, as you may think,
And when securely done,
"Now stand, dear John, upon the brink,
And I'll prepare to run.
And I'll prepare to run."

Down, down the hill the loving bride
Now came with all her force
To push him in—he stepped aside,
And she went in of course.

Now splashing, dashing like a fish,
"Oh save me, Johnny Sands."
"I can't, my dear, though much I wish,
For you have tied my hands.
For you have tied my hands."

A Little More Cider

As sung by James O'Reilly

Miss Dinah when she goes to church
She looks so neat and gay.
She has to take the dogs along
To keep the boys away.

> *Chorus :*
>
> A little more cider
> And a little more cider, too;
> A little more cider for Miss Dinah
> And we all like cider, too

Miss Dinah is a coffee pot
Her nose it is the spout;
And every time she turns around
The coffee it pours out.

> *Chorus*

Miss Dinah when she goes to bed,
She turns herself about.
She puts the candle in the bed
And blows herself right out.

> *Chorus*

Miss Dinah is an ugly bird,
She carries an ugly bill:
She lights right down in the middle of the field
And plucks out hill by hill.

Chorus

I went down to Miss Dinah's home,
Miss Dinah was a-grubbing.
She picked up a club and lit into me
And give me a devil of a clubbing.

Lucky Jim

Jim was my friend, till one unhappy day
   The usual cause—a pretty girl—came in our way.
From that day on we seemed to drift apart,
   For each aspired to win her maiden heart;
But, though I tried each art and winning wile,
   'Twas not on me she gave her sweetest smile;
Each day I saw my chances grow more slim,
   Until—to my despair—one day she married him.
             Ah, lucky Jim!
             How I envied him.

Three years passed on—long years they seemed to me—
   And then Jim died, and once more she was free.
Before me rose the bright hopes of the past;
   I wooed, I sued and married her at last.
I've got my way; and, now she is my wife,
   I know just what there is in married life;
And when I think of Jim, though underground,
   Enjoying peace and quiet most profound—
             Ah, lucky Jim!
             How I envy him.

The Boston Burglar

I was born in Bos - ton cit-y, a town you all know well, Brought up by hon - est par - ents; To you the truth I'll tell; Brought up by hon - est par - ents and raised most care - ful - ly 'Till I be - came a roving lad when I was twen - ty - three.

For burglarizing I was taken and I was sent to jail,
My friends tried to bail me out, but it was of no avail.
The judge he read my sentence, the clerk he wrote it down:
"For seven long and dreary years you are going to Jefferson Town."

To see my aged father come a-pleading to the bar,
To see my aged mother a-pulling her gray hair,
Pulling her old gray locks, my lad, and the tears come streaming down;
Said she, "My son, what have you done? You're going to Jefferson
    Town."

They put me aboard an east-bound train one cold December day,
And every station that I passed I'd hear the people say;
"There goes that Boston burglar, in chains he's bound down,
For a-robbing of a Boston bank he's going to Jefferson Town."

And there's a girl in Boston; I know she loves me well,
And if ever I regain my liberty 'tis with this girl I'll dwell;
And if ever I regain my liberty, bad company I'll shun,
I'll bid adieu to gambling, night-walking and drinking rum.

Come all you merry fellows, a warning take from me,
And never go a-night-walking and shun bad company,
For if you do, you'll surely rue, and you'll be sent like me,
For seven long and weary years to the stone penitentiary.

Fair Fanny Moore

Down in yonder cottage, all forsaken and forlorn,
The work there neglected and the grass overgrown.
Look in and you'll see some red stains upon the floor.
Alas! it is the blood of the fair Fanny Moore.

The first to come a-courting was young Randall the proud;
He offered fair Fanny his wealth and his word.
His gold and his silver all failed to secure
The heart or the hand of the fair Fanny Moore.

Then next came young Henry, of low-line degree;
He won her fond heart, and enraptured was he.
Straightway to the altar he did then secure
The heart and the hand of the fair Fanny Moore.

As Fanny was sitting in her cottage one day,
When business had called her fond husband away,
Young Randall, the traitor burst open the door,
And clasped in his arms the fair Fanny Moore.

O, Fanny, fair Fanny, reflect upon your fate;
Accept of my offer before it is too late,
There's one thing for certain, I am bound to secure
The life or the love of the fair Fanny Moore.

O, spare me; O, spare me, fair Fanny did cry;
O, spare me; O, spare me; I'm not prepared to die.
Go, then, said the traitor, to the land of the rest,
And he buried his knife in her snowy white breast.

Fair Fanny, all blooming in blood stain, she died;
Young Randall was taken, found guilty and tried;
Young Randall was hanged on a tree by the door,
For shedding the blood of the fair Fanny Moore.

Young Henry, the shepherd, went distracted and wild;
He wandered away from his own native stile;
He wandered away from his own native shore,
Lamenting the fate of the fair Fanny Moore.

He roamed through old Ireland, he roamed through old Spain,
He roamed through old England, returning home again.
At last he was taken from his own cottage door.
And laid in the grave with the fair Fanny Moore.

I've Only Been Down to the Club

As sung by James O'Reilly

Last night I was out rather late;
It was only an innocent spree.
My wife for my coming did wait
When sleeping I thought she would be.
My boots I left down in the hall
And softly I crept up the stair:
I kept rather close to the wall,
And thought to ascend unaware.
But just as I got to the door,
I seemed to get lost in the dark;
I stumbled and fell to the floor,
Just then I could only remark:

Chorus :

The club had a meeting tonight, love,
Of business we had a great sight, love,
Don't think for a moment I'm tight,
I've only been down to the club.

I found her in temper and tears,
She cried it's a sin and a shame.
She scratched both my eyes and ears,
Just then I could only explain:
She sobbed, she wept and she screamed,
She said she'd go back to her Ma;
While I on the mantel-piece leaned
And tried to enjoy my cigar.
I told her I'd buy her a dress,
If she'd leave me alone for a while;
I gave her a sweet little kiss
When I saw her beginning to smile.

Chorus

Springfield Mountain

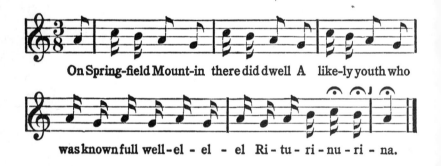

On Spring-field Mount-in there did dwell A like-ly youth who was known full well-el - el - el Ri - tu - ri - nu - ri - na.

One Monday morning he did go,
Out to the meadow for to mow.
Ri tu ri nu ri na.

A round or two and he did feel,
When a pizen serpent bit his heel
Ri tu ri nu ri na.

When he received this deadly wound,
  He dropped his scythe upon the ground.
        Ri tu ri nu ri na.

They carried him to his Polly dear,
  Which made her feel so terribly queer.
        Ri tu ri nu ri na.

And there they put him down to rest,
  And there the poor man slept his last.
        Ri tu ri nu ri na.

The tenth of August in Seventy-one,
  Was when this fateful accident was done.
        Ri tu ri nu ri na.

Let this be a warning to you all,
  To be prepared when your time does call.
        Ri tu ri nu ri na.

My Cottage by the Sea

As sung by D'Arcy Dahlberg

In my cottage by the seashore
  I can see my mountain home:
I can see the hills and valleys
  Where with pleasure I would roam.

All alone, all alone, my love has left me,
  And no other's bride I'll be,
For in my bridal robes he left me
  In my cottage by the sea.

The Hell-bound Train

A Tex - as cow - boy on a bar - room floor Had
drunk so much he could hold no more; So he
fell a - sleep with a troub - led brain, To
dream that he rode on the Hell - bound train.

The engine with murderous blood was damp
And was brilliantly lit with a brimstone lamp;
An imp, for fuel, was shoveling bones,
While the furnace rang with a thousand groans.

The boiler was filled with lager beer
And the devil himself was the engineer;
The passengers were a most motley crew,—
Church member, atheist, Gentile, and Jew.

Rich men in broadcloth, beggars in rags,
Handsome young ladies, and withered old hags,
Yellow and black men, red, brown and white,
All chained together—O God, what a sight!

While the train rushed on at an awful pace,
The sulphurous fumes scorched their hands and face;
Wider and wider the country grew,
And faster and faster the engine flew.

Louder and louder the thunder crashed
And brighter and brighter the lightning flashed;
Hotter and hotter the air became
Till the clothes were burnt from each quivering frame.

And out of the distance there arose a yell,
"Ha, ha," said the devil, "we're nearing hell!"
Then oh, how the passengers all shrieked with pain
And begged the devil to stop the train.

But he capered about and danced with glee
And laughed and joked at their misery.
"My faithful friends, you have done your work
And the devil never can pay-day shirk.

"You've bullied the weak, you've robbed the poor;
The starving brother you've turned from the door,
You've laid up gold where the canker rust,
And have given free vent to your beastly lust.

"You've justice scorned, and corruption sown,
And trampled the laws of nature down.
You have drunk, rioted, cheated, plundered and lied,
And mocked at God in your hell-born pride.

"You have paid full fare so I'll carry you through;
For it's only right you should have your due.
Why, the laborer always expects his hire,
So I'll land you safe in the lake of fire.

"Where your flesh will waste in the flames that roar,
And my imps torment you forevermore."
Then the cowboy awoke with an anguished cry,
His clothes wet with sweat and his hair standing high.

Then he prayed as he never had prayed till that hour
To be saved from his sin and the demon's power.
And his prayers and his vows were not in vain;
For he never rode the hell-bound train.

Drunkard John

You might have lit a lamp upon,
   The fiery nose of Drunkard John.
He drank so deep at Backus' bar,
   His breath for miles 'round perfumed the air.

At length his visits long protracted,
   Hath well nigh set his wife distracted,
And fiery embers dimly burned
   Before the boozy sot returned.

At length with patience quite exhausted,
   Her cruel spouse she thus accosted:
"This night you've stayed till after 'leven,
   I wish your soul were safe in heaven.

"I'd rather live in some dark cavern,
   Than see you rolling home from tavern.
If you again return so late,
   To lodge outside must be your fate."

"What, lock me out? You dare not do it,
   For if you do you'll sadly rue it;
I'll drown me in the well hard by,
   And vainly then you'll sob and sigh."

The wife replied, "My mind's at rest,
   I'm sure, dear John, you only jest."
As days rolled on the cruel fetter,
   So galled poor John he walked no better.

But heedless of his gentle wife,
  In wild excitement spent his life.
The sky now dark with many a cloud
  Had clothed the earth in evening shroud.

The moon from view was darkly hidden,
  The stars to shine were all forbidden,
When the good wife in neat attire
  Was sitting by her evening fire.

Sometimes she mused on days gone by;
  Sometimes on some misfortune nigh,
When woke the kettle from its dream
  And from the rising cloud of steam,

A song of mingled woe was heard,
  Unlike the lay of man or bird,
But when the fearful dream was gone,
  Her thoughts were fiercely fixed on John.

"He's not returned, though late the hour
  And though the heavens darkly lower
No entrance to his home he'll find,
  My plan is laid fixed in my mind."

Behold her cover up the fire,
  And softly soon to bed retire.
Refreshing sleep had scarce stole o'er
  The lady's mind when at the door

Came thumps and oaths, a horrid din,
  "Get up and let your husband in."
"Go where you may," the good wife said,
  And as she spoke her husband fled.

Crying, "You'll hear my funeral knell."
  And soon a fearful weight there fell,
And sounds of dashing water come,
  Then all was silent as a tomb.

"Poor John is drowned. Good Heavens," she cries,
  And rushing from the room she flies,
And hastens to a neighbor near,
  Her mind o'erwhelmed with grief and fear.

Cries "Fire" and "Murder" in one breath,
  "Rise up and rescue John from death.
My husband's drowning in the well,
  I heard the good man when he fell."

Her friends and sons in nature's dress,
  Ran to the place of deep distress.
All in the haste one's knee was hurt,
  When he stumbled and fell and tore his shirt.

Another bruised his tender foot at every pace,
  Till at length they reached the fatal place.
With poles and hooks the well to explore,
  They searched the bottom o'er and o'er.

But did they find the human trunk?
  No, nothing but the bucket sunk.
At last while passing through the door,
  They heard old John with laughter roar.

Who when his good wife fled with haste,
  Himself behind the well-curb placed,
Enjoyed her fright—so cruel hearted—
  And entering in as she departed,

Was safely lying in the bed,
  To hear whate'er was done or said,
And choking and giggling fit to die,
  Could not decide to laugh or cry.

I need not add though oft again,
  Poor John returned with dizzy brain,
And tarried till the latest hour,
  He never found a bolted door.

SHE SAID NOW CHILDREN STOP YOUR CRYIN'
YOU'VE GOT ANOTHER DADDY ON THE SALT LAKE LINE

AMERICAN FOLK SONG
"CASEY JONES."
ENG. BY JOHN HELD JR

THE SAILOR'S RETURN

Once I Loved a Railroad Brakeman

As sung by James O'Reilly

Once I loved a railroad brakeman,
All his thoughts they were of me;
Until a dark-haired girl persuaded him
So now he cares no more for me.

Chorus:

So go and leave me if you wish to,
Never let me cross your mind;
For in this world you love another
And to her be true and kind.

Many a night with him I rambled,
Many a night with him I spent,
I thought his heart was mine forever,
But I see it was only lent.

Chorus

Many a night he lay sleeping,
Dreaming of love's sweet repose;
While I poor girl lay broken hearted
Listening to the wind that blows.

Chorus

So farewell friends and kind relations,
Farewell to this false young man.
It was he who caused my mind to wander,
Left to mourn the best I can.

Ballad of a Young Man

As sung by Helen Ramsey

There was a young man, and he came to New York, to find him-self a lu - cra-tive po - si-tion be - fit - ting his tal - ents. And he haunt-ed all the Em-ploy-ment A-gen-cies, but was near-ly starved to death, When at last he got a job in a stone quar - ry with all the oth - er Col-lege grad - - u - ates.

And after Work was done
they lured him into a Saloon
and tempted him to drink
a glass of Beer.

But he'd promised his dear old Mother
that he never would Imbibe,
that he'd never touch his Lips to a glass
containing Liquor.

They laughed at him and Jeered
and they called him a cow-yard
Till at last he clutched and drained
the glass of Beer.

When he seen what he had Did
he dashed his glass upon the floor
and Staggered out the door
with Delirium Tremens.

And the first person that he met
was a Salvation Army Lass
and with one kick he broke
her Tambourine.

When she seen what he had Did
She placed a Mark upon his Brow
with a kick that she had learned before
she was Saved.

And the Moral of this tale
is to Shun that Fatal glass
and don't go around kicking
Other people's Tambourines.

The Dog-Catcher's Child

As sung by Helen Ramsey

Oh the moon shines to - night on the
riv - er, But not on the
dog-catch-er's child, For he fed her some raw
liv - er, And raw meat makes dog - peo-ple
wild; Now he sits all a - lone in his
man - sion, The soup drib - bles

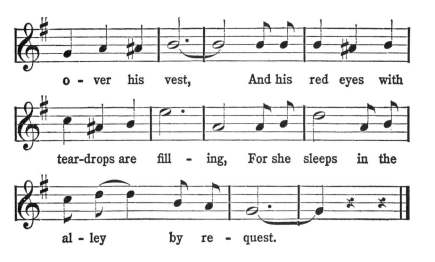

o - ver his vest, And his red eyes with

tear-drops are fill - ing, For she sleeps in the

al - ley by re - quest.

Je Donnerais Versailles

Je donnerais Versailles
Pour avoir mon ami
La Tour de Notre Dame
La Cloche de mon pays
Et ma jolie colombe
Qui chantait jour et nuit
Auprès de ma blonde
Qu'il fait bon—fait bon—fait bon
Auprès de ma blonde
Qu'il fait bon
Dormir——

The Sailor's Return

Home came the sailor, home from the sea,
And there in the stable a strange horse did see.
"O wife, now tell me what can this mean,
A strange brown horse where my mare should have been?"

"You old fool, you danged fool, you son-of-a-gun," said she,
"It's nothing but a milk cow my mother sent to me."
"Miles have I sailed, five thousand or more,
But a cow without an udder I never saw before."

Home came the sailor, home from the sea,
And there in the parlor a strange coat saw he.
"O wife, now tell me what can this mean,
A coat that's not mine where my coat should have been?"

"You old fool, you danged fool, you son-of-a-gun," said she,
"It's nothing but a blanket my mother sent to me."
"Miles have I sailed, five thousand or more,
But buttons on a blanket I never saw before."

Home came the sailor, home from the sea,
And there in his bed a strange face did see.
"O wife, now tell me what does this mean,
Another man's head where my own should have been?"

"You old fool, you danged fool, you son-of-a-gun," said she,
"It's nothing but a cabbage head my mother sent to me,"
"Miles have I sailed, five thousand or more,
But whiskers on a cabbage head I never saw before."

Note: The above is the sterilization of a ribald old ballad "Our Gude-Man" page 124, that still finds great favor among men without women. Mr. Charles J. Finger, in his "Frontier Ballads" has another version that many, like this editor, may consider far superior.

The Caissons Are Rolling Along

Artillery Song

Over hill and dale we have hit the dusty trail,
  And those caissons go rolling along.
Countermarch! Right about! Hear those wagon soldiers shout,
  While those caissons go rolling along.

Chorus :

  Oh, it's hi-hi-yee! For the field artillery,
    Shout out your numbers loud and strong.
  And where'er we go, you will always know
    That the caissons are rolling along,
      That those caissons are rolling along.

To the front, day and night, where the doughboys dig and fight,
  And those caissons go rolling along.
Our barrage will be there, fired on the rocket's red flare,
  While those caissons go rolling along.

Chorus

With the cavalry boot to boot, we will keep up the pursuit,
  And those caissons go rolling along.
To the front, day and night, where the doughboys dig and fight,
  While those caissons come rolling along.

Chorus

Young Monroe at Gerry's Rock

A Shanty Boy's Song

Come all ye true-born shan-ty-boys, wher-ev-er you may be, Come sit ye on the dea-con seat and lis-ten un-to me. I'll sing the jam on Ger-ry's Rock and a he-ro you should know, The brav-est of all shan-ty-boys, the fore-man, Young Mon-roe.

It was on a Sunday morning, as you will quickly hear,
  Our logs were piled mountain high, we could not keep them clear.
Our foreman said, "Come, cheer up lads, with hearts relieved of fear,
  We'll break the jam on Gerry's Rock and for Saginaw we'll steer."

Now some of them were willing, while others they were not,
  For to work on jams on Sunday they did not think we ought;
But six of our Canuck boys did volunteer to go
  And break the jam on Gerry's Rock, with a foreman named Monroe.

They had not rolled off many logs when they heard his clear voice say:
  "I'd have you lads on your guard, for the jam will soon give way."
These words were hardly spoken when the mass did break and go,
  And it carried off those six brave lads, and their foreman, Young
    Monroe.

When the rest of our brave shanty boys, the sad news came to hear,
  In search of their dead comrades, to the river they did steer.
Some of the mangled bodies a-floating down did go,
  While crushed and bleeding near the bank was that of Young Monroe.

They took him from his watery grave, smoothed back his raven hair;
  There was one fair girl among them whose sad cries rent the air;
There was one fair form among them, a maid from Saginaw town,
  Whose moans and cries rose to the skies, for her true lover, who'd
    gone down.

For Clara was a nice young girl, the riverman's true friend;
  She with her widowed mother dear, lived near the river's bend.
The wages of her own true love the boss to her did pay,
  And the shanty boys for her made up a generous purse next day.

They buried him with sorrow deep, 'twas on the first of May;
  Come all you brave shanty boys and for your comrade pray.
Engraved upon a hemlock tree that by the grave did grow
  Was the name and date of the sad fate of the foreman, Young Monroe.

Fair Clara did not long survive; her heart broke with her grief,
    And scarcely two months later death came to her relief.
And when this time had passed away and she was called to go,
    Her last request was granted, to rest beside Young Monroe.

Come all you brave shanty boys: I would have you call and see
    Those two green mounds by the riverside, where grows the hemlock
        tree.
The shanty boys cleared off the wood, by the lovers there laid low:
    'Twas the handsome Clara Vernon and our foreman, Young Monroe.

The Midnight Express

As sung by James O'Reilly

"Jim Blake your wife is dying!"
Came over the wires tonight:
The news was brought to the depot
By a lad nigh dead with fright.

He entered the office crying,
His face was awfully white:
"Send this to Dad on his engine,
Mother is dying tonight."

Jim Blake is our oldest driver,
He's running the midnight express:
He's pulled the throttle and lever
For most of his life I guess.

And when I saw the message
Was for my comrade Jim;
You bet I sent it in a hurry,
This sad dispatch to him.

In something less than an hour
Jim's answer came back for her.
"Tell wife I'll be there at midnight;
Tell her I am praying for her."

I left my son in the office,
Took the message to Jim's wife.
There I found a dying woman
With scarcely a breath of life.

When first I entered the chamber,
She took me at first for Jim;
She sank back nigh exhausted
When she saw it was not him.

She raised her eyes to heaven,
Her face was awful white;
She said in a dying whisper,
"God speed the express tonight."

O'er hills and dale and valley,
There thundered the midnight train.
All lighting and sobbing and throbbing
Amid the fearful strain.

But Jim hangs on to the lever,
A-guarding its crazy flight:
While a voice cried out in the darkness,
"God speed the express tonight."

In something less than an hour,
The express will be along.
And here is another message:—
"My God! There is something wrong."

Yes, here it says disaster,
The train is in a ditch.
The engineer is dying,
Derailed by an open switch.

And here is another message,
From the engineer, I guess.
"Tell wife I'll meet her in heaven,
Don't wait for the midnight express."

Bible Stories

The earth was made in six days and fin-ished on the sev-enth, Ac-cord-ing to the con-tract it should have been the 'lev-enth. The car-pen-ters got drunk and the Ma-sons would-n't work, So the cheap-est thing to do was to fill it up with dirt.

Chorus :

Old folks, young folks, everybody come,
Join the darkies' Sunday school and make yourselves at home.
Kindly check your chewing gum and razors at the door,
And we'll tell you Bible stories that you never heard before.

Adam was the first man and Eve she was his spouse;
They lost their job for stealing fruit and went to keeping house.
All was very peaceful and quiet on the main
Until a little baby came and they started raising Cain.

Chorus

The Lord made the devil, and the devil made sin;
The Lord made a cubbyhole to put the devil in.
The devil got sore and said he wouldn't stay;
The Lord said he had to, 'cause he couldn't get away.

Chorus

Cain he raised potatoes and he peddled them in town.
Abel called him hayseed every time he came around.
Cain he laid a stick of wood on brother Abel's head,
And when he took that stick away, he found poor Abel dead.

Chorus

Noah was the keeper of the Asiatic zoo;
He built an ocean liner when he hadn't much to do;
One day he got excited when the sky was getting dark,
So he gathered all his animals and put them in the ark.

Chorus

It rained for forty days and it rained for forty nights,
The water washed the land completely out of sight!
But when Noah was a-wondering as to what he'd better do
The ark hit Mount Ararat and stuck as tight as glue!

Chorus

Methuselah is famous, because he couldn't croak,
Although he finally grew to be an old and seedy bloke.
He had so many whiskers that you couldn't see his head;
If he'd lived a little longer, he'd have used them for his bed.

Chorus

Elijah was an aeronaut, or else I am a liar,
He ascended up to heaven in a chariot of fire;
His eccentric disappearance gave the Israelites a shock,
They said he beat the Wright brothers by fully half a block.

Chorus

Abraham was a patriarch, the father of his set;
He took his little Ikey out to kill him on a bet.
And he'd have met his finish if it wasn't for a lamb,
For papa had his razor out and didn't give a damn!

Chorus

Esau was a cowboy of a wild and wooly make,
His father gave him half the land and half to brother Jake;
But when he saw his title to the land it wasn't clear—
He sold it to his brother for a sandwich and a glass of beer!

Chorus

Daniel was a brave man who wouldn't mind the king;
The king he said he never heard of such a thing;
Thrust him down a man-hole with lions all beneath,
But Daniel was a dentist—and pulled the lion's teeth!

Chorus

Jonah was an emigrant, so runs the Bible tale,
He took an ocean voyage in a transatlantic whale.
The whale was over-crowded which put Jonah to distress,
So Jonah pushed the button and the whale did all the rest.

Chorus

David was a shepherd's boy, his mother's pride and joy;
His father gave him a slingshot, a harmless little toy.
Along came Goliath, a-looking for a fuss,
David heaved a cobblestone and caved in his crust.

Chorus

Samson was a strong man of the John L. Sullivan school;
He killed a thousand Philistines with the jawbone of a mule!
Along came a woman who filled him up with gin,
And shaved off his whiskers and the coppers pulled him in.

Final Chorus :

Walk in, walk in, walk in, I say,
Walk into the parlor and hear the banjos play,
Walk into the parlor and hear the banjos ring,
And see the nigger's finger a-picking on the string.

When You and I Were Young, Maggie

I wan-der'd to-day to the hill, Mag-gie , To

watch the scene be - low; The creek and the creak-ing old

mill, Mag-gie, As we used to, long a -

go. The green grove is gone from the

hill, Mag-gie, Where first the dai - sies

sprung; The creak - ing old mill is

still Mag-gie, since you and I were young.

Chorus

And now we are a-ged and gray, Mag-gie,

And the tri-als of life near-ly done;

Let us sing of the days that are gone, Mag-gie,

When you and I were young.

A city so silent and lone, Maggie,
  Where the young and the gay and the best,
In polished white mansions of stone, Maggie,
  Have each found a place of rest,
Is built where the birds used to play, Maggie,
  And join in the songs that were sung,
For we sang as gay as they, Maggie,
  When you and I were young.

Chorus

They say I am feeble with age, Maggie,
  My steps are less sprightly than then,
My face is a well-written page, Maggie,
  But time alone was the pen.
They say we are aged and gray, Maggie,
  As spray by the white breakers flung;
But to me you're as fair as you were, Maggie,
  When you and I were young.

Chorus

Seven Long Years

A variation of "The Prisoner's Song"

Seven long years I've been married,
Wished that I'd lived an old maid;
For ever since I've been married
My husband won't work at his trade.

He promised me before we were married
That I should be young and gay:
And every night of the week long
Should go to a party or play.

But I have to get up early in the morning,
Toil and toil all the day;
In the evening I have to get supper,
The dishes to wash and put away.

I go to the barroom to find him,
Bring him home if I can.
Young girls you'll never see trouble,
Until you are tied to a man.

But if I'd minded my mother
I'd be at home today.
But being so young and so foolish
The boys have led me astray.

Sometimes I live in the country,
Sometimes I live in the town;
Sometimes I have a great notion
To go to the river and drown.

I wish I had someone to love me,
Someone to call me his own;
Someone to stay with me always,
I'm tired of living alone.

If I had the wings of an angel,
More like the wings of a dove;
I'd fly far over the ocean
And rest in the arms of love.

The Letter Edged in Black

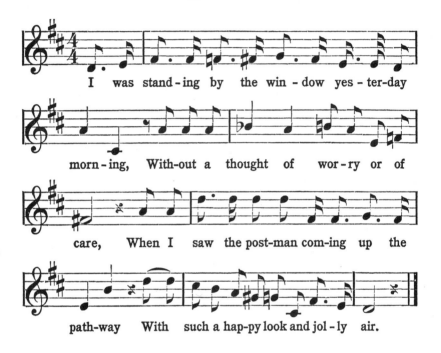

I was stand-ing by the win-dow yes-ter-day morn-ing, With-out a thought of wor-ry or of care, When I saw the post-man com-ing up the path-way With such a hap-py look and jol-ly air.

Oh, he rang the bell and whistled while he waited,
And then he said, "Good morning to you, Jack."
But he little knew the sorrow that he brought me
When he handed me a letter edged with black.

As I heard the postman whistling yester morning,
Coming down the pathway with his pack,
Oh, he little knew the sorrow that he brought me
When he handed me that letter edged in black.

With trembling hand I took the letter from him,
I broke the seal and this is what it said:
"Come home, my boy, your dear old father wants you!
Come home, my boy, your dear old mother's dead!"

I could hear the postman whistling yester morning,
Coming down the pathway with his pack,
But he little knew the sorrow that he brought me
When he handed me that letter edged in black.

"The last words that your mother ever uttered—
'Tell my boy I want him to come back,'
My eyes are blurred, my poor old heart is breaking,
For I'm writing you this letter edged in black."

I could hear the postman whistling yester morning,
Coming down the pathway with his pack,
But he little knew the sorrow that he brought me
When he handed me that letter edged in black.

I bow my head in sorrow and in silence,
The sunshine of my life it all has fled,
Since the postman brought that letter yester morning
Saying, "Come home, my boy, your poor old mother's dead!"

I could hear the postman whistling yester morning,
Coming down the pathway with his pack,
But he little knew the sorrow that he brought me
When he handed me that letter edged in black.

"Those angry words, I wish I'd never spoken,
You know I never meant them, don't you, Jack?
May the angels bear me witness, I am asking
Your forgiveness in this letter edged in black."

I could hear the postman whistling yester morning,
Coming down the pathway with his pack,
But he little knew the sorrow that he brought me
When he handed me that letter edged in black.

I'll Give My Love a Cherry

(Southern Mountain Ballad)

As sung by Margaret Marshall

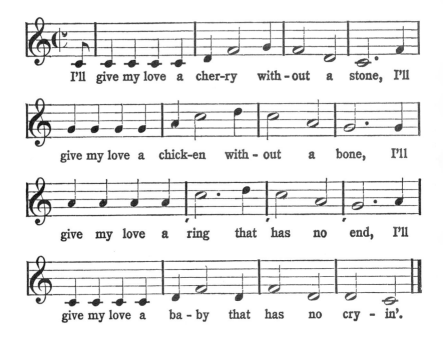

I'll give my love a cher-ry with-out a stone, I'll give my love a chick-en with-out a bone, I'll give my love a ring that has no end, I'll give my love a ba-by that has no cry - in'.

How can there be a cherry without a stone?
How can there be a chicken without a bone?
How can there be a ring that has no end?
How can there be a baby that has no cryin'?

A cherry in the bloom, it has no stone,
A chicken in the egg, it has no bone,
A ring that's rolling, it has no end,
A baby when it's sleepin', it has no cryin'.

Jim Fisk, Jr.

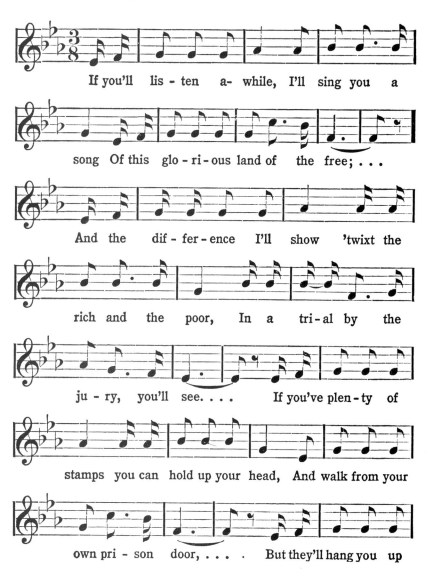

If you'll lis - ten a- while, I'll sing you a
song Of this glo - ri - ous land of the free; . . .
And the dif - fer - ence I'll show 'twixt the
rich and the poor, In a tri - al by the
ju - ry, you'll see. . . . If you've plen - ty of
stamps you can hold up your head, And walk from your
own pri - son door, ... But they'll hang you up

high, if you've no friends or gold, Let the

rich go, but hang up the poor. . . .

Refrain

In the tri - als for mur-der we have now - a -

days, The rich ones get off swift and sure. . . .

If you've thou-sands to pay to the ju - ry and judge,

You may bet they'll go back on the poor. . . .

Let me speak of a great man who is now in the grave,
    As good a man as ever was born.
Jim Fisk he was called and his money he gave
    To the outcast, the poor and forlorn.
We all know that he loved both women and wine,
    But his heart it was right, I am sure;
He lived like a prince in his palace so fine,
    But he never went back on the poor.

Jim Fisk was a man, wore his heart on his sleeve,
  No matter what people would say:
He did all his deeds, both the good and the bad,
  In the broad open light of the day:
With his grand six-in-hand at the beach at Long Branch,
  He cut a big dash, to be sure.
But Chicago's big fire showed the world that Jim Fisk
  With his wealth still remembered the poor.

When the telegram came that the poor and distressed
  Were starving to death, slow but sure,
By the lightning express, sent by noble Jim Fisk,
  Went food for the hungry and poor.
Now what do you think of the trial of Stokes,
  Who murdered this friend of the poor?
If such men go free, is any one safe
  To step from outside their own door?

Is there one law for the rich and one for the poor?
  It seems so, at least so they say;
But if they hang up the poor, why hadn't the rich
  Ought to swing up in the very same way?
Don't show any favor to friend or to foe,
  The beggar or prince at your door.
But the millionaire you must hang up also,
  And never go back on the poor.

What's the Use?

As sung by Raymond Hitchcock

Some call this the best old world that nature could contrive,
One thing's sure, that none of us get out of it alive.
Things go on year after year in much the same old style,
Makes you sometimes wonder if anything's worthwhile.
No one knows just where the world is going to so fast,
Life's a great conundrum which we will give up at last.
All the dreaming, all the scheming since the days of yore
Seem to land us just precisely where we were before.

 So what's the use of people growing old and dying if we must be
  born again?
 O what's the use of all these cunning little babies growing up to
  homely men?
 O what's the use of lending any one a five-spot if the next time he
  borrows ten?
 All single folks 'tis said often wish that they were wed
 And those who are wish they were dead.
  So what's the use?

What's the use of drinking if you always have a thirst?
Twenty drinks will make you far more thirsty than the first.
Seems to me to take a bath is quite a hopeless case!
You'll get dirty once again and wash the same old face!

What's the use of giving good advice to people now?
Wise men need it not and fools don't take it anyhow.
Take the straight and narrow path, the parsons always say.
What's the use of telling that to the people on Broadway.

 So what's the use of fellows having lots of push if some one else
  has got the pull?
 O what's the use of speculating all your cash, if you're a bear you
  make a bull?
 O what's the use of people saying you're a bear if then they fleece
  you for your wool?
 It's the old bull con, you are a lamb and later on you are a lobster
  when it's gone,
  So what's the use?

Get Away, Old Man, Get Away!

Now listen all you girls when you go to choose a man,
  Don't take one who is ancient, get a young one if you can.
For an old man he is old, and an old man he is gray,
  But a young man knows just how to love—
      Get away, old man, get away!

Don't ever marry an old man, you'll find it doesn't pay,
  For you'll soon meet a young man, who will steal your heart away.
For an old man, etc.

You want to find a young man with healthy rosy cheeks,
  For if an old man gets the rheumatiz he stays in bed for weeks.
For an old man, etc.

I wouldn't marry an old man, I'll tell you the reason why,
  Tobacco juice is on his lips and his chin is never dry.
For an old man, etc.

I'd rather marry a young man with a goodly supply of brains,
  For there's no fool like an old fool and you cannot make him change.
For an old man, etc.

An old man may have money and cattle for his farm,
  But a young man hugs much better for there is power in his arm.
For an old man, etc.

An old man and a young girl should never, never mix,
  For no one ever found out how to teach an old dog new tricks.
For an old man, etc.

Be sure to marry a young man no matter what the cost,
  For an old man's like an apple when bitten by the frost.
For an old man he is old, and an old man he is gray,
  But a young man knows just how to love—
      Get away, old man, get away!

Dis Mornin', Dis Evenin', So Soon

As Sung by William B. Smith, and nicely, too

Tell old Bill, when he leaves home dis morn-in',

Tell old Bill, when he leaves home dis eve-nin',

Tell old Bill, when he leaves home, To let dem down-town

coons a-lone, Dis morn-in', dis eve-nin', so soon.

Bill left home by de alley gate, dis mornin',
Bill left home by de alley gate, dis evenin',
Bill left home by de alley gate,
But he couldn't outrun that thirty-eight!
Dis mornin', dis evenin', so soon.

Old Bill's wife was a-bakin' bread, dis mornin,'
Old Bill's wife was a-bakin' bread, dis evenin',
Old Bill's wife was a-bakin' bread,
When they told her Bill had been shot dead
Dis mornin', dis evenin', so soon.

Oh no, dat can't be so, dis mornin',
Oh no, dat can't be so, dis evenin',
Oh no, dat can't be so:
For Bill lef' home but an hour ago,
Dis mornin', dis evenin', so soon.

Oh no, dat cannot be, dis mornin',
Oh no, dat cannot be, dis evenin',
Oh no, dat cannot be,
For to shoot my husban' in de firs' degree,
Dis mornin', dis evenin', so soon.

Dey brought Bill home wid his toe-nails draggin', dis mornin',
Dey brought Bill home wid his toe-nails draggin', dis evenin',
Dey brought Bill home wid his toe-nails draggin',
Dey was taking Bill home in de hurry-up wagon,
Dis mornin', dis evenin', so soon.

The Dying Ranger

As sung by D'Arcy Dahlberg

The sun was sink-ing in the west, And fell with lin-g'ring ray Through the branches of the for-est, . . Where a wound-ed ran-ger lay; 'Neath the shade of a pal-met-to . . . And the sun-set sil-v'ry sky, Far a-way from his home in Tex-as . . . They laid him down to die.

A group had gathered round him,
His comrades in the fight,
A tear rolled down each man's cheek
As he bid a last good-night.
One tried and true companion
Was kneeling by his side,
To stop his life-blood flowing,
But alas, in vain he tried.

When to stop the life-blood flowing
He found 'twas all in vain,
The tears rolled down each man's cheek
Like light showers of rain.
Up spoke the noble ranger,
"Boys, weep no more for me,
I am crossing the deep waters
To a country that is free

"Draw closer to me, comrades,
And listen to what I say,
I am going to tell a story
While my spirit hastens away.
Way back in Northwest Texas,
That good old Lone Star State,
There is one that for my coming
With a weary heart will wait.

"A fair young girl, my sister,
My only joy, my pride,
She was my friend from boyhood,
I had no one left beside.
I have loved her as a brother,
And with a father's care
I have strove from grief and sorrow
Her gentle heart to spare.

"My mother, she lies sleeping
Beneath the church-yard sod,
And many a day has passed away
Since her spirit fled to God.
My father, he lies sleeping
Beneath the deep blue sea,
I have no other kindred,
There are none but Nell and me.

"But our country was invaded
And they called for volunteers;
She threw her arms around me,
Then burst into tears,
Saying, 'Go, my darling brother,
Drive those traitors from our shore,
My heart may need your presence,
But our country needs you more.'

"It is true I love my country,
For her I gave my all.
If it hadn't been for my sister,
I would be content to fall.
I am dying, comrades, dying,
She will never see me more,
But in vain she'll wait my coming
By our little cabin door.

"Comrades, gather closer
And listen to my dying prayer:
Who will be to her as a brother,
And shield her with a brother's care?"
Up spake the noble rangers,
They answered one and all,
"We will be to her as brothers
Till the last one does fall."

One glad smile of pleasure
O'er the ranger's face was spread;
One dark, convulsive shudder
And the ranger boy was dead.
Far from his darling sister
We laid him down to rest
With his saddle for a pillow
And his gun across his breast.

Shanahan's Ould Shebeen

By Gerald Brennan

This is the tale that Cassidy told
In his halls a-sheen with purple and gold:
  —Told as he sprawled in an easy chair,
  Chewing cigars at a dollar a pair.
  —told with a sigh and perchance a tear
  As the rough soul showed through the cracked veneer;
  —Told as he gazed on the walls near by,
  Where a Greuze and a Millet were hung on high,
  With a rude little print in a frame between—
A picture of Shanahan's old shebeen.

"I'm drinkin' me mornin's mornin'—but it doesn't taste the same;
Though the glass is iv finest crystal, an' the liquor slips down like crame;
An' me cockney footman brings it on a soort of a silver plate,—
Sherry and bitters it is; whiskey is out iv date.
In me bran' new brownstone manshin'—Fift' av'noo over th' way,
Th' Cathedral round th' corner, an' the Lord Archbishop to tay,
Sure I ought to be sthiff with grandeur, but me tastes are mighty mean,
An' I'd rather a mornin's mornin' at Shanahan's ould shebeen.

"Oh! well do I mind th' shanty—th' rocks, an' the field beyant,
The dirt floor yellow wid sawdust, an' th' walls on a three-inch shlant.
There's a twelve-story 'flat' on th' site now—('twas meself that builded
    the same),

An' they called it 'The Mont-morincy'—though I wanted the good
   ould name.
Me dinner-pail under me oxther, before th' whistle blew,
I'd banish th' drames from me eyelids wid a noggin', or maybe two;
An' oh! 'twas th' illigant whisky—its like I have never seen
Since I went for me mornin's mornin' to Shanahan's ould shebeen.

"I disremember th' makers—I couldn't tell you th' brand;
But it smiled like the golden sunlight, an' it looked an' tasted gr-rand.
When me throat was caked with morthar an' me head was cracked wid
   a blast,
One drink o' Shanahan's dewdrops an' all me troubles was past.
That's why, as I squat on th' cushins, wid divil a hap'orth to do,
In a mornin' coat lined wid velvit, an' a champagne lunch at two,
The' mem'ry comes like a banshee meself an' me wealth between;
An' I long for a mornin's mornin' in Shanahan's ould shebeen.

"A mornin' coat lined wid velvit—an' me ould coat used to do
Alike for mornin' an' evenin' (an' sometimes I slep' in it, too),
An' 'twas divil a sup iv sherry that Shanahan kept—no fear;
If you couldn't afford good whisky, he'd take you on trust for beer.
Th' dacintest gang I knew there—McCarthy (Sinathor since),
An' Murphy that mixed th' morthar (sure th' Pope has made him a
   Prince),
You should see 'em, avic, o' Sundays, wid faces scraped an' clean,
When th' boss stood a mornin's mornin' round Shanahan's ould
   shebeen.

"Whist!—here comes his Grace's carriage; 'twill be lunchtime by an'
   by;
An' I dasn't drink another, though me throat is powerful dry;
For I've got to meet th' Archbishop—I'm a laborer now no more,
—But, ohone! those were fine times, then, lad, an' to talk o' 'em makes
   me sore.
An' whisper—there's times, I tell you, when I'd swap this easy chair,
An' the velvit coat, an' th' footman, wid his Sassenach nose in th' air,
—An th' Lord Archbishop himself, too, for a drink o' th' days that ha'
   been,
For th' taste o' a mornin's mornin' in Shanahan's ould shebeen."

Sally Brown

O Sal - ly Brown she's a bright mu - lat - ta,
Way - ay, roll and go! O she drinks rum and
chews to - bac - ca, Spend my mon-ey on Sal - ly Brown.

Seven long years I courted Sally.
She said, "O boy, why do you dally?"

Oh Sally Brown, I long to see you!
Oh Sally Brown, I'll not deceive you!

Sally Brown's a creole lady;
I guess she's got a yellow baby.

Oh Sally Brown, what is the matter?
Pretty gal, but can't get at her.

Oh Sally lives on the old plantation,
A member of the creole nation.

Now all my troubles they are over,
   Way-ay, roll and go!

Sally's married to a cullud soldier,
   I'll spend no money on Sally Brown.

The Recruit

By Robert William Chambers

Sez Corporal Madden to Private McFadden:
"Bedad, yer a bad'un!
Now, turn out yer toes
Yer belt is unhookit!
Yer cap is on crookit!
Ye may not be dhrunk,
But, be-jabers, ye look it.
    Wan,—two!
    Wan,—two!
Ye monkey-face divil, I'll jolly ye through!
    Wan,—two!
    Time! Mark!
Ye march like an aigle in Cintheral Park!"

Sez Corporal Madden to Private McFadden:
"A saint it ud sadden
To drill such a mug!
Eyes front! ye baboon, ye.
Ye've jaws like a goat,—
Halt! ye leather-lipped loon, ye!
    Wan,—two!
    Wan,—two!
Ye whiskered ourang-outang, I'll fix you!
    Wan,—two!
    Time! Mark!
Ye've eyes like a bat!
Can ye see in the dark?"

Sez Corporal Madden to Private McFadden:
"Yer figger wants padd'n—
Sure, man, ye've no shape!
Behin' ye, yer shoulders stick out like two bowlders;

Yer shins is as thin
As a pair of pen-holders.
    Wan,—two!
    Wan,—two!
Yer belly belongs on yer back, it do!
    Wan,—two!
    Time! Mark!
I'm as dhry as a dog,—I can't shpake, but I bark!"

Sez Corporal Madden to Private McFadden:
"Me heart it ud gladden
To blacken yer eye,
Yer getting too bold, ye
Compel me to scold ye,—
'Tis 'Halt' that I say—
Will ye heed what I told ye?
    Wan,—two!
    Wan,—two!
Be-jabers I'm dhrier than Brian Boru!
    Wan,—two!
    Time! Mark!
What's wu'ruk for chickens is sport for a lark!"

Sez Corporal Madden to Private McFadden:
"I'll not stay a-gadd'n
With monkeys like you!
I'll travel no farther,
I'm dying for wather;—
Come on, if ye like—
Can ye loan me a quarter!
    Ya-as, you,
    What? two?
And ye'll pay the potheen? Ye're a daisy. Whurroo!
    You'll do!
    Whist! Mark!
The Rigimint's flattered to own ye, me spark!"

The Flying Cloud

My name is Ed - ward Hall - a - han and

you must un - der - stand   I came from Coun-ty

Wat - er - ford and   Ire - land's hap - py   land.

When I was young and   in   my prime, fair

For - tune   on   me smiled,   My   par - ents reared

me ten - der - ly; I   was   their   on - ly child.

My father bound me to a trade in Waterford's fair town,
He bound me to a cooper there, by the name of William Brown.
I served my master faithfully for eighteen months or more,
Then I shipped on board of the Ocean Queen, belonging to Tramore.

When we came unto Bermuda's isle, there I met with Captain Moore,
The commander of the Flying Cloud, hailing from Baltimore;
He asked me if I'd ship with him, on a slaving voyage to go,
To the burning shores of Africa, where the sugar cane does grow.

It was after some week's sailing we arrived on Africa's shore,
And five hundred of those poor slaves, my boys, from their native land
　　we bore
We made them walk in on a plank, and we stowed them down below;
Scarce eighteen inches to a man was all they had to go.

The plague and fever came on board, swept half of them away;
We dragged the bodies up on deck and hove them in the sea.
It was better for the rest of them that they had died before,
Than to work under brutes of planters in Cuba forevermore.

It was after stormy weather we arrived off Cuba's shore,
And we sold them to the planters there to be slaves forevermore.
For the rice and the coffee seed to sow beneath the broiling sun,
There to lead a wretched lonely life till their career was run.

It's now our money is all spent, we must go to sea again,
When Captain Moore he came on deck and said unto us men,
"There is gold and silver to be had with me you'll remain,
And we'll hoist the pirate flag aloft, and we'll scour the Spanish Main."

We all agreed but three young men who told us them to land,
And two of them were Boston boys, the other from Newfoundland.
I wish to God I'd joined those men and went with them on shore,
Than to lead a wild and reckless life, serving under Captain Moore.

The Flying Cloud was a Yankee ship of five hundred tons or more:
She could outsail any clipper ship hailing out of Baltimore.
With her canvas white as the driven snow, and on it there's no specks,
And forty men and fourteen guns she carried on her decks.

It's oft I've seen that gallant ship with the wind abaft her beam,
With her royals and her stunsails set, a sight for to be seen;
With the curling waves at her clipper bow, a sailor's joy to feel,
And the canvas taut in the whistling breeze, logging fourteen off the
    reel.

We sank and plundered many a ship down on the Spanish Main,
Caused many a wife and orphan in sorrow to remain;
To them we gave no quarter, but gave them watery graves,
For the saying of our captain was that dead men tell no tales.

Pursued we were by many a ship, by frigates and liners too,
Till at last a British man-o'-war, the Dungeness, hove in view,
She fired a shot across our bow, as we sailed before the wind,
Till a chainshot cut our mainmast down, and we fell far behind.

Our crew they beat to quarters as she ranged up along-side,
And soon across our quarter-deck there ran a crimson tide.
We fought till Captain Moore was killed and twenty of our men,
Till a bombshell set our ship on fire, we had to surrender then.

It's next to Newgate we were brought, bound down in iron chains,
For the sinking and the plundering of ships on the Spanish Main.
The judge he found us guilty, we were condemned to die;
Young men, a warning by me take, and shun all piracy.

Then fare you well, old Waterford, and the girl I adore;
I'll never kiss your cheek again, or squeeze your hand no more.
For whiskey and bad company first made a wretch of me;
Young men, a warning by me take, and shun all piracy.

The Girl in the Blue Velvet Band

In that city of wealth, beauty and fashion;
Dear old 'Frisco, where I first saw the light,
And the many frolics that I had there
Are still in my memory tonight.

One evening while out for a ramble;
Here or there without thought or design,
I chanced on a young girl, tall and slender,
At the corner of Kearney and Pine.

On her face was the first flush of nature,
And bright eyes seemed to expand;
While her hair fell in rich, brilliant tresses,
Was entwined in a blue velvet band.

To a house of gentle ruination,
She invited me with a sweet smile;
She seemed so refined, gay and charming
That I thought I would tarry awhile.

She then shared with me a collection
Of wines of an excellent brand,
And conversed in the politest language;
The girl with the blue velvet band. ·

After lunch to a well-kept apartment,
We repaired to the third floor above;
And I thought myself truly in heaven,
Where reigneth the Goddess of Love.

Her lady's taste was resplendent,
From the graceful arrangement of things;
From the pictures that stood on the bureau,
To the little bronze Cupid with wings.

But what struck me most was an object
Designed by an artistic hand;
'Twas the costly layout of a hop-fiend,
And the fiend was my blue velvet band.

On a pile of soft robes and pillows
She reclined, I declined on the floor,
Then we both hit the pipe and I slumbered,
I pondered it over and o'er.

'Tis months since the craven arm grasped me,
And in bliss did my life glide away;
From opium to 'dipping' and thieving,
She artfully led day by day.

One evening, coming home wet and weary,
With the swag from a jewelry store;
I heard the soft voice of my loved one,
As I gently opened the door.

"If you'll give me a clue to convict him,"
Said a stranger, in tones soft and bland,
"You'll then prove to me that you love me."
"It's a go," said my blue velvet band.

Ah! How my heart filled with anger,
At woman, so fair, false, and vile,
And to think that I once truly adored her,
Brought to my lips a contemptuous smile.

All ill-gotten gains we had squandered
And my life was hers to command;
Betrayed and deserted for another—
Could this be my blue velvet band?

Just few moments before I was hunted
By the cops, who wounded me, too,
And my temper was none the sweetest,
As I swung myself into their view.

And the copper, not liking the glitter
Of the "44" Colt in my hand,
Hurriedly left through the window,
Leaving me with my blue velvet band.

What happened to me I will tell you:
I was ditched for a desperate crime,
There was hell in a bank about midnight,
And my pal was shot down in his prime.

As a convict of hard reputation,
Ten years of hard grind I did land,
And I often thought of the pleasures
I had with my blue velvet band.

One night as bed time was ringing,
I was standing close to the bars,
I fancied I heard a girl singing,
Far out in the ocean of stars.

Her voice had the same touch of sadness
I knew that but one could command,
I had the same thrill of gladness
As that of my blue velvet band.

Many months have passed since this happened,
And the story belongs to the past;
I forgave her, but just retribution
Claimed this fair but false one at last.

She slowly sank lower and lower,
Down through life's shifting sands,
Till finally she died in a hop joint,
This girl with the blue velvet band.

If she had been true when I met her,
A bright future for us was in store,
For I was an able mechanic,
And honest and square to the core.

But as sages of old have contended,
What's decreed we mortals must stand;
So a grave in the Potter's field ended
My romance with the blue velvet band.

Now, when I get out I will hasten
Back to my home town again,
Where my chances are good for some dollars,
All the way from a thousand to ten.

And if I'm in luck I'll endeavor
To live honest in some other land,
And bid farewell to dear old 'Frisco,
And the grave of my blue velvet band.

The Millman Tragedy

By Mrs. C. A. Barron

Lines on the death of William Millman, who was executed at Charlotte-town, P. E. I., on April 10, 1888, for the foul murder of Mary Tuplin.

Both old and young, come ponder well, what I shall now relate
Of this most awful tragedy in Charlottetown of late:
The murderer, of whom I write, few years beyond a boy,
William Millman was his name, his mother's hope and joy.

She brought him up so tenderly, and did a mother's part,
Nor dreamed that time so near at hand, when he would break her heart;
Yes, break both parents' hearts—I can't describe the sorrow they must
feel,
No matter where on earth they go, their griefs are with them still.

The memory of that much-loved son, his mother's eyes behold.
With murder of the deepest dye on his immortal soul:
To look upon that fine young man, no one would e'er have thought
So horrible a crime as that would enter his young heart.

Against the girl whom he had vowed he never would deceive.
Poor innocent! She could do naught but his false vows believe.
Shame on the base deceiver, whose cruel heart was bent
On taking her poor life away—for that was his intent.

It is of her I now must speak, her cruel death recall.
Her broken-hearted parents dear, the saddest thought of all.
Their hearts were filled with grief, for they were mourning for their son.
And while their tears were falling fast, this dreadful deed was done.

'Twas Mary Tuplin, young and fair—her household duties o'er,
Went forth to meet her lover, as she oft had done before:
And as she tripped along the path, one look at home she cast,
Though in her heart she never dreamed that it would be her last.

Her thoughts were sad, for brother dear—alas! 'twas that same day
She stood beside his silent grave and saw him laid away;
The tears were fresh upon her cheeks as she went on her way,
Anxious to meet with him she loved, to wipe those tears away.

She hoped that he would share her grief, perhaps her thoughts had been
That if his heart were sore depressed, how she would comfort him.
But not a man, a monster, worse, a demon, waited there;
A monster would not raise his hand to one so young and fair.

They met, poor girl, what horrid fate, what anguish did she bear;
Could her poor rigid corpse but speak, alas! what should we hear?
What agonizing cries and prayers to him her life to spare,
As with the weapon in his hand—she sees the pistol near.

Her fair young life he took, and when the last faint spark was gone,
He to the river dragged her then, tied to a heavy stone;
And as he cast her body in, he slyly looked around,
Saying, "No one will ever think of this; she never will be found."

But O, the eye of God was on his every movement there,
And soon before the neighbors He all traces did lay bare;
Her body was discovered soon, beneath the flowing wave,
At the botton of the river he had planned to be her grave.

Her parents laid her in the tomb, close by her brother's side,
Their happiness forever gone, their peace of mind denied;
O, cruel-hearted, false young man, who led that girl astray,
And baser still, to hide his sin, he took her life away.

Now pray, young men, a warning take, from friends who wish you well,
Remember Millman, while he lay, chained in his lonely cell;
Think of his anguish and despair, when told that he must die,
That he must pay the forfeit for the laws that he'd defy.

Think of your parents and of his, their hearts, what grief they know;
They never can look up again in this world of sin and woe;

Think of that young girl, who did on his promise rely,
Whom he sent to meet her Maker—all unprepared to die.

And all young girls who read these lines, before it is too late,
Be cautious in your conduct, lest you meet the same sad fate;
And when in company with men, be prudent and take care,
Put no temptation in their way—of flatterers beware.

They may seem kind and loving words, they whisper in your ear,
But seek advice from those who know, to judge if they're sincere;
And mothers who have children dear, O, every day and hour,
Pray to the God, who rules above, to keep them by His power.

Now ponder well, young people all, and pray this warning take,
Be careful in your friendships and choose a proper mate;
Honor your dear parents, and keep the laws divine,
And happiness and peace will be your portion for all time.

The Closing Scene

From Millman's eyes the streaming tears in bitter anguish fell,
While to his friends and all he knew he bade a last farewell;
Then "Cover up my eyes," he said, "that I may never see
The gallows, or that dreadful rope that now awaiteth me."

Poor Millman paid the penalty—he lies beneath the sod;
We leave him to the tender mercies of a most loving God.

In Bohemia Hall

Harmony a la SETH CLARK

In Bo - he - mia Hall, in Bo - he - mia Hall Where

ev - 'ry man is King. In Bo - he - mia Hall, in Bo -

he - mia Hall We'll laugh, we'll drink, we'll sing,   With a

big stein on the ta - ble, We'll drink while we are

a - ble, And we don't give a damn for

rit.

any old man In Bo - he - mia Hall.

The Actor's Story

By George E. Simmons

Mine is a wild, strange story, the strangest you ever heard;
There are many who won't believe it, but it's gospel, every word;
It's the biggest drama of any in a long, adventurous life;
The scene was a ship, and the actors were myself and my new-wed wife.

You mustn't mind if I ramble and lose the thread now and then;
I'm old, you know, and I wander—it's a way with old women and men.
For their lives all lie behind them, and their thoughts go far away,
And are tempted afield, like children lost on a Summer day.

The years must be five-and-twenty that have passed since that awful
    night,
But I see it again this evening; I can never shut out the sight.
We were only a few weeks married; I and the wife, you know,
When we had an offer for Melbourne, and made up our minds to go.

We'd acted together in England, traveling up and down
With a strolling band of players, going from town to town;
We played the lovers together—we were leading lady and gent—
And at last we played in earnest and straight to the church we went.

The parson gave us his blessing, and I gave Nellie the ring.
And swore that I'd love and cherish and endow her with everything;
How we smiled at that part of the service, when I said "I thee endow."
But as to the "love and cherish," friend, I meant to keep that vow.

We were only a couple of strollers; we had coin when the show was good.
When it wasn't we went without it, and we did the best we could;
We were happy and loved each other, and laughed at the shifts we made.
Where love makes plenty of sunshine there poverty casts no shade.

Well, at last we got to London, and did pretty well for a bit;
Then the business dropped to nothing and the manager took a fit—

Stepped off one Sunday morning, forgetting the treasury call;
But our luck was in, and we managed right on our feet to fall.

We got an offer for Melbourne—got it that very week.
Those were the days when thousands went over their fortunes to seek—
The days of the great gold fever, and a manager thought the spot
Good for a "spec," and took us actors among his lot.

We hadn't a friend in England—we'd only ourselves to please—
And we jumped at the chance of trying our fortune across the seas.
We went on a sailing vessel, and the journey was long and rough;
We hadn't been out a fortnight before we had had enough.

But use is a second nature, and we'd got not to mind a storm.
When misery came upon us—came in a hideous form.
My poor little wife fell ailing, grew worse, and at last so bad
That the doctor said she was dying—I thought 'twould have sent me
    mad.

Dying, where leagues of billows seemed to shriek for their prey,
And the nearest land was hundreds—aye, thousands of miles away.
She raved one night in a fever, and the next lay still as death,
So still I'd bend to listen for the faintest sign of breath.

She seemed in a sleep, and sleeping with a smile on her thin, wan face,
She passed away one morning, while I prayed to the throne of grace.
I knelt in the little cabin, and prayer after prayer I said
Till the surgeon came and told me it was useless—my wife was dead!

Dead! I wouldn't believe it. They forced me away that night,
For I raved in my wild despairing, the shock sent me mad outright,
I was shut in the farthest cabin, and I beat my head on the side,
And all day long in my madness, "They've murdered her!" I cried.

They locked me away from my fellows—put me in cruel chains.
It seems I had seized a weapon to beat out the surgeon's brains;
I cried in my wild, mad fury that he was the devil sent
To gloat o'er the frenzied anguish with which my heart was rent.

I spent that night with the irons heavy upon my wrists;
And my wife lay dead quite near me. I beat with my fettered fists,
Beat at my prison panels, and then, O God! and then
I heard the shrieks of women and the tramp of hurrying men.

I heard the cry, "Ship afire!" caught up by a hundred throats,
And over the roar the captain shouting to lower the boats;
Then cry upon cry, and curses, and the crackle of burning wood,
And the place grew hot as a furnace—I could feel it where I stood.

I beat at the door and shouted, but never a sound came back,
And the timbers above me started, till right through a yawning crack
I could see the flames shooting upward, seizing on mast and sail,
Fanned in their burning fury by the breath of the howling gale.

I dashed at the door in fury, shrieking, "I will not die!
Die in this burning prison!"—but I caught no answering cry.
Then, suddenly, right upon me the flames crept up with a roar,
And their fiery tongues shot forward, cracking my prison door.

I was free—with the heavy iron door dragging me down to death,
I fought my way to the cabin, choked with the burning breath
Of the flames that danced around me like mad, mocking fiends at play,
And then—O God! I can see it, and shall to my dying day.

There lay my Nell as they'd left her, dead in her berth that night;
The flames flung a smile on her features—a horrible, lurid light.
God knows how I reached and touched her, but I found myself by her
     side;
I thought she was living a moment; I forgot that my Nell had died.

In the shock of those awful seconds reason came back to my brain,
I heard a sound as of breathing, and then a low cry of pain.
O, was there mercy in Heaven? Was there a God in the skies?
The dead woman's lips were moving, the dead woman opened her eyes.

I cursed like a madman raving—I cried to her, "Nell, my Nell!"
They had left us alone and helpless, alone in that burning hell;

They had left us alone to perish—forgotten me living—and she
Had been left for the fire to bear her to Heaven, instead of the sea.

I clutched her, roused her, shrieking, the stupor was on her still;
I seized her in spite of my fetters—fear gave me a giant's will.
God knows how I did it, but blindly I fought through the flames and
    the wreck,
Up, up to the air, and brought her to the deck.

We'd a moment of life together—a moment of life, the time
For one last word to each other—'twas a moment, supreme, sublime.
From the trance we'd for death mistaken the heat had brought her to
    life,
And I was fettered and helpless—so we lay there, husband and wife!

It was but a moment, but ages seemed to have pased away,
When a shout came over the water, and I looked, and lo, there lay
Right away from the vessel, a boat that was standing by,
They had seen our forms on the vessel as the flames lit up the sky.

I shouted a prayer to Heaven, they called for my wife, and she
Tore with new strength at my fetters—God helped her and I was free;
Then over the burning bulwarks we leaped for one chance of life.
Did they save us? Well, here I am, sir, and yonder's my dear old wife.

We were out in the boat till daylight, when a great ship passing by
Took us on board and at Melbourne landed us by and by.
We've played many parts in dramas since we went on that famous trip,
But ne'er such a scene together as we had on the burning ship!

THE PRIZE FIGHT

Index of Song Titles

Index of First Lines and Choruses

CATALOGUE OF DOVER BOOKS

Books Explaining Science and Mathematics

WHAT IS SCIENCE?, N. Campbell. The role of experiment and measurement, the function of mathematics, the nature of scientific laws, the difference between laws and theories, the limitations of science, and many similarly provocative topics are treated clearly and without technicalities by an eminent scientist. "Still an excellent introduction to scientific philosophy," H. Margenau in PHYSICS TODAY. "A first-rate primer . . . deserves a wide audience," SCIENTIFIC AMERICAN. 192pp. 5⅜ x 8.   S43 Paperbound **$1.25**

THE NATURE OF PHYSICAL THEORY, P. W. Bridgman. A Nobel Laureate's clear, non-technical lectures on difficulties and paradoxes connected with frontier research on the physical sciences. Concerned with such central concepts as thought, logic, mathematics, relativity, probability, wave mechanics, etc. he analyzes the contributions of such men as Newton, Einstein, Bohr, Heisenberg, and many others. "Lucid and entertaining . . . recommended to anyone who wants to get some insight into current philosophies of science," THE NEW PHILOSOPHY. Index. xi + 138pp. 5⅜ x 8.   S33 Paperbound **$1.25**

EXPERIMENT AND THEORY IN PHYSICS, Max Born. A Nobel Laureate examines the nature of experiment and theory in theoretical physics and analyzes the advances made by the great physicists of our day: Heisenberg, Einstein, Bohr, Planck, Dirac, and others. The actual process of creation is detailed step-by-step by one who participated. A fine examination of the scientific method at work. 44pp. 5⅜ x 8.   S308 Paperbound **75¢**

THE PSYCHOLOGY OF INVENTION IN THE MATHEMATICAL FIELD, J. Hadamard. The reports of such men as Descartes, Pascal, Einstein, Poincaré, and others are considered in this investigation of the method of idea-creation in mathematics and other sciences and the thinking process in general. How do ideas originate? What is the role of the unconscious? What is Poincaré's forgetting hypothesis? are some of the fascinating questions treated. A penetrating analysis of Einstein's thought processes concludes the book. xiii + 145pp. 5⅜ x 8.   T107 Paperbound **$1.25**

THE NATURE OF LIGHT AND COLOUR IN THE OPEN AIR, M. Minnaert. Why are shadows sometimes blue, sometimes green, or other colors depending on the light and surroundings? What causes mirages? Why do multiple suns and moons appear in the sky? Professor Minnaert explains these unusual phenomena and hundreds of others in simple, easy-to-understand terms based on optical laws and the properties of light and color. No mathematics is required but artists, scientists, students, and everyone fascinated by these "tricks" of nature will find thousands of useful and amazing pieces of information. Hundreds of observational experiments are suggested which require no special equipment. 200 illustrations; 42 photos. xvi + 362pp. 5⅜ x 8.   T196 Paperbound **$2.00**

THE UNIVERSE OF LIGHT, W. Bragg. Sir William Bragg, Nobel Laureate and great modern physicist, is also well known for his powers of clear exposition. Here he analyzes all aspects of light for the layman: lenses, reflection, refraction, the optics of vision, x-rays, the photoelectric effect, etc. He tells you what causes the color of spectra, rainbows, and soap bubbles, how magic mirrors work, and much more. Dozens of simple experiments are described. Preface. Index. 199 line drawings and photographs, including 2 full-page color plates. x + 283pp. 5⅜ x 8.   T538 Paperbound **$1.85**

SOAP-BUBBLES: THEIR COLOURS AND THE FORCES THAT MOULD THEM, C. V. Boys. For continuing popularity and validity as scientific primer, few books can match this volume of easily-followed experiments, explanations. Lucid exposition of complexities of liquid films, surface tension and related phenomena, bubbles' reaction to heat, motion, music, magnetic fields. Experiments with capillary attraction, soap bubbles on frames, composite bubbles, liquid cylinders and jets, bubbles other than soap, etc. Wonderful introduction to scientific method, natural laws that have many ramifications in areas of modern physics. Only complete edition in print. New Introduction by S. Z. Lewin, New York University. 83 illustrations; 1 full-page color plate. xii + 190pp. 5⅜ x 8½.   T542 Paperbound **95¢**

CATALOGUE OF DOVER BOOKS

THE STORY OF X-RAYS FROM RONTGEN TO ISOTOPES, A. R. Bleich, M.D. This book, by a member of the American College of Radiology, gives the scientific explanation of x-rays, their applications in medicine, industry and art, and their danger (and that of atmospheric radiation) to the individual and the species. You learn how radiation therapy is applied against cancer, how x-rays diagnose heart disease and other ailments, how they are used to examine mummies for information on diseases of early societies, and industrial materials for hidden weaknesses. 54 illustrations show x-rays of flowers, bones, stomach, gears with flaws, etc. 1st publication. Index. xix + 186pp. 5⅜ x 8.   T622 Paperbound **$1.35**

SPINNING TOPS AND GYROSCOPIC MOTION, John Perry. A classic elementary text of the dynamics of rotation — the behavior and use of rotating bodies such as gyroscopes and tops. In simple, everyday English you are shown how quasi-rigidity is induced in discs of paper, smoke rings, chains, etc., by rapid motions; why a gyrostat falls and why a top rises; precession; how the earth's motion affects climate; and many other phenomena. Appendix on practical use of gyroscopes. 62 figures. 128pp. 5⅜ x 8.   T416 Paperbound **$1.00**

SNOW CRYSTALS, W. A. Bentley, M. J. Humphreys. For almost 50 years W. A. Bentley photographed snow flakes in his laboratory in Jericho, Vermont; in 1931 the American Meteorological Society gathered together the best of his work, some 2400 photographs of snow flakes, plus a few ice flowers, windowpane frosts, dew, frozen rain, and other ice formations. Pictures were selected for beauty and scientific value. A very valuable work to anyone in meteorology, cryology; most interesting to layman; extremely useful for artist who wants beautiful, crystalline designs. All copyright free. Unabridged reprint of 1931 edition. 2453 illustrations. 227pp. 8 x 10½.   T287 Paperbound **$3.00**

A DOVER SCIENCE SAMPLER, edited by George Barkin. A collection of brief, non-technical passages from 44 Dover Books Explaining Science for the enjoyment of the science-minded browser. Includes work of Bertrand Russell, Poincaré, Laplace, Max Born, Galileo, Newton; material on physics, mathematics, metallurgy, anatomy, astronomy, chemistry, etc. You will be fascinated by Martin Gardner's analysis of the sincere pseudo-scientist, Moritz's account of Newton's absentmindedness, Bernard's examples of human vivisection, etc. Illustrations from the Diderot Pictorial Encyclopedia and De Re Metallica. 64 pages.   **FREE**

THE STORY OF ATOMIC THEORY AND ATOMIC ENERGY, J. G. Feinberg. A broader approach to subject of nuclear energy and its cultural implications than any other similar source. Very readable, informal, completely non-technical text. Begins with first atomic theory, 600 B.C. and carries you through the work of Mendelejeff, Röntgen, Madame Curie, to Einstein's equation and the A-bomb. New chapter goes through thermonuclear fission, binding energy, other events up to 1959. Radioactive decay and radiation hazards, future benefits, work of Bohr, moderns, hundreds more topics. "Deserves special mention . . . not only authoritative but thoroughly popular in the best sense of the word," Saturday Review. Formerly, "The Atom Story." Expanded with new chapter. Three appendixes. Index. 34 illustrations. vii + 243pp. 5⅜ x 8.   T625 Paperbound **$1.45**

THE STRANGE STORY OF THE QUANTUM, AN ACCOUNT FOR THE GENERAL READER OF THE GROWTH OF IDEAS UNDERLYING OUR PRESENT ATOMIC KNOWLEDGE, B. Hoffmann. Presents lucidly and expertly, with barest amount of mathematics, the problems and theories which led to modern quantum physics. Dr. Hoffmann begins with the closing years of the 19th century, when certain trifling discrepancies were noticed, and with illuminating analogies and examples takes you through the brilliant concepts of Planck, Einstein, Pauli, Broglie, Bohr, Schroedinger, Heisenberg, Dirac, Sommerfeld, Feynman, etc. This edition includes a new, long postscript carrying the story through 1958. "Of the books attempting an account of the history and contents of our modern atomic physics which have come to my attention, this is the best," H. Margenau, Yale University, in "American Journal of Physics." 32 tables and line illustrations. Index. 275pp. 5⅜ x 8.   T518 Paperbound **$1.50**

SPACE AND TIME, E. Borel. Written by a versatile mathematician of world renown with his customary lucidity and precision, this introduction to relativity for the layman presents scores of examples, analogies, and illustrations that open up new ways of thinking about space and time. It covers abstract geometry and geographical maps, continuity and topology, the propagation of light, the special theory of relativity, the general theory of relativity, theoretical researches, and much more. Mathematical notes. 2 Indexes. 4 Appendices. 15 figures. xvi + 243pp. 5⅜ x 8.   T592 Paperbound **$1.45**

FROM EUCLID TO EDDINGTON: A STUDY OF THE CONCEPTIONS OF THE EXTERNAL WORLD, Sir Edmund Whittaker. A foremost British scientist traces the development of theories of natural philosophy from the western rediscovery of Euclid to Eddington, Einstein, Dirac, etc. The inadequacy of classical physics is contrasted with present day attempts to understand the physical world through relativity, non-Euclidean geometry, space curvature, wave mechanics, etc. 5 major divisions of examination: Space; Time and Movement; the Concepts of Classical Physics; the Concepts of Quantum Mechanics; the Eddington Universe. 212pp. 5⅜ x 8.   T491 Paperbound **$1.35**

Nature, Biology

NATURE RECREATION: Group Guidance for the Out-of-doors, William Gould Vinal. Intended for both the uninitiated nature instructor and the education student on the college level, this complete "how-to" program surveys the entire area of nature education for the young. Philosophy of nature recreation; requirements, responsibilities, important information for group leaders; nature games; suggested group projects; conducting meetings and getting discussions started; etc. Scores of immediately applicable teaching aids, plus completely updated sources of information, pamphlets, field guides, recordings, etc. Bibliography. 74 photographs. + 310pp. 5⅜ x 8½. T1015 Paperbound **$1.75**

HOW TO KNOW THE WILD FLOWERS, Mrs. William Starr Dana. Classic nature book that has introduced thousands to wonders of American wild flowers. Color-season principle of organization is easy to use, even by those with no botanical training, and the genial, refreshing discussions of history, folklore, uses of over 1,000 native and escape flowers, foliage plants are informative as well as fun to read. Over 170 full-page plates, collected from several editions, may be colored in to make permanent records of finds. Revised to conform with 1950 edition of Gray's Manual of Botany. xlii + 438pp. 5⅜ x 8½. T332 Paperbound **$1.85**

HOW TO KNOW THE FERNS, F. T. Parsons. Ferns, among our most lovely native plants, are all too little known. This classic of nature lore will enable the layman to identify almost any American fern he may come across. After an introduction on the structure and life of ferns, the 57 most important ferns are fully pictured and described (arranged upon a simple identification key). Index of Latin and English names. 61 illustrations and 42 full-page plates. xiv + 215pp. 5⅜ x 8. T740 Paperbound **$1.35**

MANUAL OF THE TREES OF NORTH AMERICA, Charles Sprague Sargent. Still unsurpassed as most comprehensive, reliable study of North American tree characteristics, precise locations and distribution. By dean of American dendrologists. Every tree native to U.S., Canada, Alaska, 185 genera, 717 species, described in detail—leaves, flowers, fruit, winterbuds, bark, wood, growth habits etc. plus discussion of varieties and local variants, immaturity variations. Over 100 keys, including unusual 11-page analytical key to genera, aid in identification. 783 clear illustrations of flowers, fruit, leaves. An unmatched permanent reference work for all nature lovers. Second enlarged (1926) edition. Synopsis of families. Analytical key to genera. Glossary of technical terms. Index. 783 illustrations, 1 map. Two volumes. Total of 982pp. 5⅜ x 8. T277 Vol. I Paperbound **$2.00**
T278 Vol. II Paperbound **$2.00**
The set **$4.00**

TREES OF THE EASTERN AND CENTRAL UNITED STATES AND CANADA, W. M. Harlow. A revised edition of a standard middle-level guide to native trees and important escapes. More than 140 trees are described in detail, and illustrated with more than 600 drawings and photographs. Supplementary keys will enable the careful reader to identify almost any tree he might encounter. xiii + 288pp. 5⅜ x 8. T395 Paperbound **$1.35**

GUIDE TO SOUTHERN TREES, Ellwood S. Harrar and J. George Harrar. All the essential information about trees indigenous to the South, in an extremely handy format. Introductory essay on methods of tree classification and study, nomenclature, chief divisions of Southern trees, etc. Approximately 100 keys and synopses allow for swift, accurate identification of trees. Numerous excellent illustrations, non-technical text make this a useful book for teachers of biology or natural science, nature lovers, amateur naturalists. Revised 1962 edition. Index. Bibliography. Glossary of technical terms. 920 illustrations; 201 full-page plates. ix + 709pp. 4⅝ x 6⅜. T945 Paperbound **$2.25**

FRUIT KEY AND TWIG KEY TO TREES AND SHRUBS, W. M. Harlow. Bound together in one volume for the first time, these handy and accurate keys to fruit and twig identification are the only guides of their sort with photographs (up to 3 times natural size). "Fruit Key": Key to over 120 different deciduous and evergreen fruits. 139 photographs and 11 line drawings. Synoptic summary of fruit types. Bibliography. 2 Indexes (common and scientific names). "Twig Key": Key to over 160 different twigs and buds. 173 photographs. Glossary of technical terms. Bibliography. 2 Indexes (common and scientific names). Two volumes bound as one. Total of xvii + 126pp. 5⅜ x 8⅜. T511 Paperbound **$1.25**

INSECT LIFE AND INSECT NATURAL HISTORY, S. W. Frost. A work emphasizing habits, social life, and ecological relations of insects, rather than more academic aspects of classification and morphology. Prof. Frost's enthusiasm and knowledge are everywhere evident as he discusses insect associations and specialized habits like leaf-rolling, leaf-mining, and case-making, the gall insects, the boring insects, aquatic insects, etc. He examines all sorts of matters not usually covered in general works, such as: insects as human food, insect music and musicians, insect response to electric and radio waves, use of insects in art and literature. The admirably executed purpose of this book, which covers the middle ground between elementary treatment and scholarly monographs, is to excite the reader to observe for himself. Over 700 illustrations. Extensive bibliography. x + 524pp. 5⅜ x 8. T517 Paperbound **$2.45**

CATALOGUE OF DOVER BOOKS

COMMON SPIDERS OF THE UNITED STATES, J. H. Emerton. Here is a nature hobby you can pursue right in your own cellar! Only non-technical, but thorough, reliable guide to spiders for the layman. Over 200 spiders from all parts of the country, arranged by scientific classification, are identified by shape and color, number of eyes, habitat and range, habits, etc. Full text, 501 line drawings and photographs, and valuable introduction explain webs, poisons, threads, capturing and preserving spiders, etc. Index. New synoptic key by S. W. Frost. xxiv + 225pp. 5⅜ x 8.　　　　　　　　　　　　　　　　　　　　　　　　　T223 Paperbound **$1.35**

THE LIFE STORY OF THE FISH: HIS MANNERS AND MORALS, Brian Curtis. A comprehensive, non-technical survey of just about everything worth knowing about fish. Written for the aquarist, the angler, and the layman with an inquisitive mind, the text covers such topics as evolution, external covering and protective coloration, physics and physiology of vision, maintenance of equilibrium, function of the lateral line canal for auditory and temperature senses, nervous system, function of the air bladder, reproductive system and methods—courtship, mating, spawning, care of young—and many more. Also sections on game fish, the problems of conservation and a fascinating chapter on fish curiosities. "Clear, simple language . . . excellent judgment in choice of subjects . . . delightful sense of humor," New York Times. Revised (1949) edition. Index. Bibliography of 72 items. 6 full-page photographic plates. xii + 284pp. 5⅜ x 8.　　　　　　　　　　　　T929 Paperbound **$1.50**

BATS, Glover Morrill Allen. The most comprehensive study of bats as a life-form by the world's foremost authority. A thorough summary of just about everything known about this fascinating and mysterious flying mammal, including its unique location sense, hibernation and cycles, its habitats and distribution, its wing structure and flying habits, and its relationship to man in the long history of folklore and superstition. Written on a middle-level, the book can be profitably studied by a trained zoologist and thoroughly enjoyed by the layman. "An absorbing text with excellent illustrations. Bats should have more friends and fewer thoughtless detractors as a result of the publication of this volume," William Beebe, Books. Extensive bibliography. 57 photographs and illustrations. x + 368pp. 5⅜ x 8½.　　　　　　　　　　　　　　　　　　　　　　　　　　T984 Paperbound **$2.00**

BIRDS AND THEIR ATTRIBUTES, Glover Morrill Allen. A fine general introduction to birds as living organisms, especially valuable because of emphasis on structure, physiology, habits, behavior. Discusses relationship of bird to man, early attempts at scientific ornithology, feathers and coloration, skeletal structure including bills, legs and feet, wings. Also food habits, evolution and present distribution, feeding and nest-building, still unsolved questions of migrations and location sense, many more similar topics. Final chapter on classification, nomenclature. A good popular-level summary for the biologist; a first-rate introduction for the layman. Reprint of 1925 edition. References and index. 51 illustrations. viii + 338pp. 5⅜ x 8½.　　　　　　　　　　　　　　　　　　　　　　　T957 Paperbound **$1.85**

LIFE HISTORIES OF NORTH AMERICAN BIRDS, Arthur Cleveland Bent. Bent's monumental series of books on North American birds, prepared and published under auspices of Smithsonian Institute, is the definitive coverage of the subject, the most-used single source of information. Now the entire set is to be made available by Dover in inexpensive editions. This encyclopedic collection of detailed, specific observations utilizes reports of hundreds of contemporary observers, writings of such naturalists as Audubon, Burroughs, William Brewster, as well as author's own extensive investigations. Contains literally everything known about life history of each bird considered: nesting, eggs, plumage, distribution and migration, voice, enemies, courtship, etc. These not over-technical works are musts for ornithologists, conservationists, amateur naturalists, anyone seriously interested in American birds.

BIRDS OF PREY. More than 100 subspecies of hawks, falcons, eagles, buzzards, condors and owls, from the common barn owl to the extinct caracara of Guadaloupe Island. 400 photographs. Two volume set. Index for each volume. Bibliographies of 403, 520 items. 197 full-page plates. Total of 907pp. 5⅜ x 8½.　　　　　　　　Vol. I　T931 Paperbound **$2.50**
　　　　　　　　　　　　　　　　　　　　　　　　　　　　　　Vol. II　T932 Paperbound **$2.50**

WILD FOWL. Ducks, geese, swans, and tree ducks—73 different subspecies. Two volume set. Index for each volume. Bibliographies of 124, 144 items. 106 full-page plates. Total of 685pp. 5⅜ x 8½.　　　　　　　　　　　　　　　　　　Vol. I　T285 Paperbound **$2.50**
　　　　　　　　　　　　　　　　　　　　　　　　　　　　　　Vol. II　T286 Paperbound **$2.50**

SHORE BIRDS. 81 varieties (sandpipers, woodcocks, plovers, snipes, phalaropes, curlews, oyster catchers, etc.). More than 200 photographs of eggs, nesting sites, adult and young of important species. Two volume set. Index for each volume. Bibliographies of 261, 188 items. 121 full-page plates. Total of 860pp. 5⅜ x 8½.　　　Vol. I　T933 Paperbound **$2.35**
　　　　　　　　　　　　　　　　　　　　　　　　　　　　　　Vol. II　T934 Paperbound **$2.35**

THE LIFE OF PASTEUR, R. Vallery-Radot. 13th edition of this definitive biography, cited in Encyclopaedia Britannica. Authoritative, scholarly, well-documented with contemporary quotes, observations; gives complete picture of Pasteur's personal life; especially thorough presentation of scientific activities with silkworms, fermentation, hydrophobia, inoculation, etc. Introduction by Sir William Osler. Index. 505pp. 5⅜ x 8.　　　　　T632 Paperbound **$2.00**

Puzzles, Mathematical Recreations

SYMBOLIC LOGIC and THE GAME OF LOGIC, Lewis Carroll. "Symbolic Logic" is not concerned with modern symbolic logic, but is instead a collection of over 380 problems posed with charm and imagination, using the syllogism, and a fascinating diagrammatic method of drawing conclusions. In "The Game of Logic" Carroll's whimsical imagination devises a logical game played with 2 diagrams and counters (included) to manipulate hundreds of tricky syllogisms. The final section, "Hit or Miss" is a lagniappe of 101 additional puzzles in the delightful Carroll manner. Until this reprint edition, both of these books were rarities costing up to $15 each. Symbolic Logic: Index. xxxi + 199pp. The Game of Logic: 96pp. 2 vols. bound as one. 5⅜ x 8. T492 Paperbound **$1.50**

PILLOW PROBLEMS and A TANGLED TALE, Lewis Carroll. One of the rarest of all Carroll's works, "Pillow Problems" contains 72 original math puzzles, all typically ingenious. Particularly fascinating are Carroll's answers which remain exactly as he thought them out, reflecting his actual mental process. The problems in "A Tangled Tale" are in story form, originally appearing as a monthly magazine serial. Carroll not only gives the solutions, but uses answers sent in by readers to discuss wrong approaches and misleading paths, and grades them for insight. Both of these books were rarities until this edition, "Pillow Problems" costing up to $25, and "A Tangled Tale" $15. Pillow Problems: Preface and Introduction by Lewis Carroll. xx + 109pp. A Tangled Tale: 6 illustrations. 152pp. Two vols. bound as one. 5⅜ x 8. T493 Paperbound **$1.50**

AMUSEMENTS IN MATHEMATICS, Henry Ernest Dudeney. The foremost British originator of mathematical puzzles is always intriguing, witty, and paradoxical in this classic, one of the largest collections of mathematical amusements. More than 430 puzzles, problems, and paradoxes. Mazes and games, problems on number manipulation, unicursal and other route problems, puzzles on measuring, weighing, packing, age, kinship, chessboards, joiners', crossing river, plane figure dissection, and many others. Solutions. More than 450 illustrations. vii + 258pp. 5⅜ x 8. T473 Paperbound **$1.25**

THE CANTERBURY PUZZLES, Henry Dudeney. Chaucer's pilgrims set one another problems in story form. Also Adventures of the Puzzle Club, the Strange Escape of the King's Jester, the Monks of Riddlewell, the Squire's Christmas Puzzle Party, and others. All puzzles are original, based on dissecting plane figures, arithmetic, algebra, elementary calculus and other branches of mathematics, and purely logical ingenuity. "The limit of ingenuity and intricacy," The Observer. Over 110 puzzles. Full Solutions. 150 illustrations. vii + 225pp. 5⅜ x 8. T474 Paperbound **$1.25**

MATHEMATICAL EXCURSIONS, H. A. Merrill. Even if you hardly remember your high school math, you'll enjoy the 90 stimulating problems contained in this book and you will come to understand a great many mathematical principles with surprisingly little effort. Many useful shortcuts and diversions not generally known are included: division by inspection, Russian peasant multiplication, memory systems for pi, building odd and even magic squares, square roots by geometry, dyadic systems, and many more. Solutions to difficult problems. 50 illustrations. 145pp. 5⅜ x 8. T350 Paperbound **$1.00**

MAGIC SQUARES AND CUBES, W. S. Andrews. Only book-length treatment in English, a thorough non-technical description and analysis. Here are nasik, overlapping, pandiagonal, serrated squares; magic circles, cubes, spheres, rhombuses. Try your hand at 4-dimensional magical figures! Much unusual folklore and tradition included. High school algebra is sufficient. 754 diagrams and illustrations. viii + 419pp. 5⅜ x 8. T658 Paperbound **$1.85**

CALIBAN'S PROBLEM BOOK: MATHEMATICAL, INFERENTIAL AND CRYPTOGRAPHIC PUZZLES, H. Phillips (Caliban), S. T. Shovelton, G. S. Marshall. 105 ingenious problems by the greatest living creator of puzzles based on logic and inference. Rigorous, modern, piquant; reflecting their author's unusual personality, these intermediate and advanced puzzles all involve the ability to reason clearly through complex situations; some call for mathematical knowledge, ranging from algebra to number theory. Solutions. xi + 180pp. 5⅜ x 8. T736 Paperbound **$1.25**

MATHEMATICAL PUZZLES FOR BEGINNERS AND ENTHUSIASTS, G. Mott-Smith. 188 mathematical puzzles based on algebra, dissection of plane figures, permutations, and probability, that will test and improve your powers of inference and interpretation. The Odic Force, The Spider's Cousin, Ellipse Drawing, theory and strategy of card and board games like tit-tat-toe, go moku, salvo, and many others. 100 pages of detailed mathematical explanations. Appendix of primes, square roots, etc. 135 illustrations. 2nd revised edition. 248pp. 5⅜ x 8. T198 Paperbound **$1.00**

MATHEMAGIC, MAGIC PUZZLES, AND GAMES WITH NUMBERS, R. V. Heath. More than 60 new puzzles and stunts based on the properties of numbers. Easy techniques for multiplying large numbers mentally, revealing hidden numbers magically, finding the date of any day in any year, and dozens more. Over 30 pages devoted to magic squares, triangles, cubes, circles, etc. Edited by J. S. Meyer. 76 illustrations. 128pp. 5⅜ x 8. T110 Paperbound **$1.00**

CATALOGUE OF DOVER BOOKS

THE BOOK OF MODERN PUZZLES, G. L. Kaufman. A completely new series of puzzles as fascinating as crossword and deduction puzzles but based upon different principles and techniques. Simple 2-minute teasers, word labyrinths, design and pattern puzzles, logic and observation puzzles — over 150 braincrackers. Answers to all problems. 116 illustrations. 192pp. 5⅜ x 8.
T143 Paperbound **$1.00**

NEW WORD PUZZLES, G. L. Kaufman. 100 ENTIRELY NEW puzzles based on words and their combinations that will delight crossword puzzle, Scrabble and Jotto fans. Chess words, based on the moves of the chess king; design-onyms, symmetrical designs made of synonyms; rhymed double-crostics; syllable sentences; addle letter anagrams; alphagrams; linkograms; and many others all brand new. Full solutions. Space to work problems. 196 figures. vi + 122pp. 5⅜ x 8.
T344 Paperbound **$1.00**

MAZES AND LABYRINTHS: A BOOK OF PUZZLES, W. Shepherd. Mazes, formerly associated with mystery and ritual, are still among the most intriguing of intellectual puzzles. This is a novel and different collection of 50 amusements that embody the principle of the maze: mazes in the classical tradition; 3-dimensional, ribbon, and Möbius-strip mazes; hidden messages; spatial arrangements; etc.—almost all built on amusing story situations. 84 illustrations. Essay on maze psychology. Solutions. xv + 122pp. 5⅜ x 8.
T731 Paperbound **$1.00**

MAGIC TRICKS & CARD TRICKS, W. Jonson. Two books bound as one. 52 tricks with cards, 37 tricks with coins, bills, eggs, smoke, ribbons, slates, etc. Details on presentation, misdirection, and routining will help you master such famous tricks as the Changing Card, Card in the Pocket, Four Aces, Coin Through the Hand, Bill in the Egg, Afghan Bands, and over 75 others. If you follow the lucid exposition and key diagrams carefully, you will finish these two books with an astonishing mastery of magic. 106 figures. 224pp. 5⅜ x 8. T909 Paperbound **$1.00**

PANORAMA OF MAGIC, Milbourne Christopher. A profusely illustrated history of stage magic, a unique selection of prints and engravings from the author's private collection of magic memorabilia, the largest of its kind. Apparatus, stage settings and costumes; ingenious ads distributed by the performers and satiric broadsides passed around in the streets ridiculing pompous showmen; programs; decorative souvenirs. The lively text, by one of America's foremost professional magicians, is full of anecdotes about almost legendary wizards: Dede, the Egyptian; Philadelphia, the wonder-worker; Robert-Houdin, "the father of modern magic;" Harry Houdini; scores more. Altogether a pleasure package for anyone interested in magic, stage setting and design, ethnology, psychology, or simply in unusual people. A Dover original. 295 illustrations; 8 in full color. Index. viii + 216pp. 8⅜ x 11¼.
T774 Paperbound **$2.25**

HOUDINI ON MAGIC, Harry Houdini. One of the greatest magicians of modern times explains his most prized secrets. How locks are picked, with illustrated picks and skeleton keys; how a girl is sawed into twins; how to walk through a brick wall — Houdini's explanations of 44 stage tricks with many diagrams. Also included is a fascinating discussion of great magicians of the past and the story of his fight against fraudulent mediums and spiritualists. Edited by W.B. Gibson and M.N. Young. Bibliography. 155 figures, photos. xv + 280pp. 5⅜ x 8.
T384 Paperbound **$1.25**

MATHEMATICS, MAGIC AND MYSTERY, Martin Gardner. Why do card tricks work? How do magicians perform astonishing mathematical feats? How is stage mind-reading possible? This is the first book length study explaining the application of probability, set theory, theory of numbers, topology, etc., to achieve many startling tricks. Non-technical, accurate, detailed! 115 sections discuss tricks with cards, dice, coins, knots, geometrical vanishing illusions, how a Curry square "demonstrates" that the sum of the parts may be greater than the whole, and dozens of others. No sleight of hand necessary! 135 illustrations. xii + 174pp. 5⅜ x 8.
T335 Paperbound **$1.00**

EASY-TO-DO ENTERTAINMENTS AND DIVERSIONS WITH COINS, CARDS, STRING, PAPER AND MATCHES, R. M. Abraham. Over 300 tricks, games and puzzles will provide young readers with absorbing fun. Sections on card games; paper-folding; tricks with coins, matches and pieces of string; games for the agile; toy-making from common household objects; mathematical recreations; and 50 miscellaneous pastimes. Anyone in charge of groups of youngsters, including hard-pressed parents, and in need of suggestions on how to keep children sensibly amused and quietly content will find this book indispensable. Clear, simple text, copious number of delightful line drawings and illustrative diagrams. Originally titled "Winter Nights Entertainments." Introduction by Lord Baden Powell. 329 illustrations. v + 186pp. 5⅜ x 8½.
T921 Paperbound **$1.00**

STRING FIGURES AND HOW TO MAKE THEM, Caroline Furness Jayne. 107 string figures plus variations selected from the best primitive and modern examples developed by Navajo, Apache, pygmies of Africa, Eskimo, in Europe, Australia, China, etc. The most readily understandable, easy-to-follow book in English on perennially popular recreation. Crystal-clear exposition; step-by-step diagrams. Everyone from kindergarten children to adults looking for unusual diversion will be endlessly amused. Index. Bibliography. Introduction by A. C. Haddon. 17 full-page plates. 960 illustrations. xxiii + 401pp. 5⅜ x 8½.
T152 Paperbound **$2.00**

Entertainments, Humor

ODDITIES AND CURIOSITIES OF WORDS AND LITERATURE, C. Bombaugh, edited by M. Gardner. The largest collection of idiosyncratic prose and poetry techniques in English, a legendary work in the curious and amusing bypaths of literary recreations and the play technique in literature—so important in modern works. Contains alphabetic poetry, acrostics, palindromes, scissors verse, centos, emblematic poetry, famous literary puns, hoaxes, notorious slips of the press, hilarious mistranslations, and much more. Revised and enlarged with modern material by Martin Gardner. 368pp. 5⅜ x 8. **T759 Paperbound $1.50**

A NONSENSE ANTHOLOGY, collected by Carolyn Wells. 245 of the best nonsense verses ever written, including nonsense puns, absurd arguments, mock epics and sagas, nonsense ballads, odes, "sick" verses, dog-Latin verses, French nonsense verses, songs. By Edward Lear, Lewis Carroll, Gelett Burgess, W. S. Gilbert, Hilaire Belloc, Peter Newell, Oliver Herford, etc., 83 writers in all plus over four score anonymous nonsense verses. A special section of limericks, plus famous nonsense such as Carroll's "Jabberwocky" and Lear's "The Jumblies" and much excellent verse virtually impossible to locate elsewhere. For 50 years considered the best anthology available. Index of first lines specially prepared for this edition. Introduction by Carolyn Wells. 3 indexes: Title, Author, First lines. xxxiii + 279pp. **T499 Paperbound $1.35**

THE BAD CHILD'S BOOK OF BEASTS, MORE BEASTS FOR WORSE CHILDREN, and A MORAL ALPHABET, H. Belloc. Hardly an anthology of humorous verse has appeared in the last 50 years without at least a couple of these famous nonsense verses. But one must see the entire volumes—with all the delightful original illustrations by Sir Basil Blackwood—to appreciate fully Belloc's charming and witty verses that play so subacidly on the platitudes of life and morals that beset his day—and ours. A great humor classic. Three books in one. Total of 157pp. 5⅜ x 8. **T749 Paperbound $1.00**

THE DEVIL'S DICTIONARY, Ambrose Bierce. Sardonic and irreverent barbs puncturing the pomposities and absurdities of American politics, business, religion, literature, and arts, by the country's greatest satirist in the classic tradition. Epigrammatic as Shaw, piercing as Swift, American as Mark Twain, Will Rogers, and Fred Allen, Bierce will always remain the favorite of a small coterie of enthusiasts, and of writers and speakers whom he supplies with "some of the most gorgeous witticisms of the English language" (H. L. Mencken). Over 1000 entries in alphabetical order. 144pp. 5⅜ x 8. **T487 Paperbound $1.00**

THE PURPLE COW AND OTHER NONSENSE, Gelett Burgess. The best of Burgess's early nonsense, selected from the first edition of the "Burgess Nonsense Book." Contains many of his most unusual and truly awe-inspiring pieces: 36 nonsense quatrains, the Poems of Patagonia, Alphabet of Famous Goops, and the other hilarious (and rare) adult nonsense that place him in the forefront of American humorists. All pieces are accompanied by the original Burgess illustrations. 123 illustrations. xiii + 113pp. 5⅜ x 8. **T772 Paperbound $1.00**

MY PIOUS FRIENDS AND DRUNKEN COMPANIONS and MORE PIOUS FRIENDS AND DRUNKEN COMPANIONS, Frank Shay. Folksingers, amateur and professional, and everyone who loves singing: here, available for the first time in 30 years, is this valued collection of 132 ballads, blues, vaudeville numbers, drinking songs, sea chanties, comedy songs. Songs of pre-Beatnik Bohemia; songs from all over America, England, France, Australia; the great songs of the Naughty Nineties and early twentieth-century America. Over a third with music. Woodcuts by John Held, Jr. convey perfectly the brash insouciance of an era of rollicking unabashed song. 12 illustrations by John Held, Jr. Two indexes (Titles and First lines and Choruses). Introductions by the author. Two volumes bound as one. Total of xvi + 235pp. 5⅜ x 8½. **T946 Paperbound $1.00**

HOW TO TELL THE BIRDS FROM THE FLOWERS, R. W. Wood. How not to confuse a carrot with a parrot, a grape with an ape, a puffin with nuffin. Delightful drawings, clever puns, absurd little poems point out far-fetched resemblances in nature. The author was a leading physicist. Introduction by Margaret Wood White. 106 illus. 60pp. 5⅜ x 8. **T523 Paperbound 75¢**

PECK'S BAD BOY AND HIS PA, George W. Peck. The complete edition, containing both volumes, of one of the most widely read American humor books. The endless ingenious pranks played by bad boy "Hennery" on his pa and the grocery man, the outraged pomposity of Pa, the perpetual ridiculing of middle class institutions, are as entertaining today as they were in 1883. No pale sophistications or subtleties, but rather humor vigorous, raw, earthy, imaginative, and, as folk humor often is, sadistic. This peculiarly fascinating book is also valuable to historians and students of American culture as a portrait of an age. 100 original illustrations by True Williams. Introduction by E. F. Bleiler. 347pp. 5⅜ x 8. **T497 Paperbound $1.35**

CATALOGUE OF DOVER BOOKS

THE HUMOROUS VERSE OF LEWIS CARROLL. Almost every poem Carroll ever wrote, the largest collection ever published, including much never published elsewhere: 150 parodies, burlesques, riddles, ballads, acrostics, etc., with 130 original illustrations by Tenniel, Carroll, and others. "Addicts will be grateful . . . there is nothing for the faithful to do but sit down and fall to the banquet," N. Y. Times. Index to first lines. xiv + 446pp. 5⅜ x 8.
T654 Paperbound **$1.85**

DIVERSIONS AND DIGRESSIONS OF LEWIS CARROLL. A major new treasure for Carroll fans! Rare privately published humor, fantasy, puzzles, and games by Carroll at his whimsical best, with a new vein of frank satire. Includes many new mathematical amusements and recreations, among them the fragmentary Part III of "Curiosa Mathematica." Contains "The Rectory Umbrella," "The New Belfry," "The Vision of the Three T's," and much more. New 32-page supplement of rare photographs taken by Carroll. x + 375pp. 5⅜ x 8.
T732 Paperbound **$1.65**

THE COMPLETE NONSENSE OF EDWARD LEAR. This is the only complete edition of this master of gentle madness available at a popular price. A BOOK OF NONSENSE, NONSENSE SONGS, MORE NONSENSE SONGS AND STORIES in their entirety with all the old favorites that have delighted children and adults for years. The Dong With A Luminous Nose, The Jumblies, The Owl and the Pussycat, and hundreds of other bits of wonderful nonsense. 214 limericks, 3 sets of Nonsense Botany, 5 Nonsense Alphabets, 546 drawings by Lear himself, and much more. 320pp. 5⅜ x 8.
T167 Paperbound **$1.00**

THE MELANCHOLY LUTE, The Humorous Verse of Franklin P. Adams ("FPA"). The author's own selection of light verse, drawn from thirty years of FPA's column, "The Conning Tower," syndicated all over the English-speaking world. Witty, perceptive, literate, these ninety-six poems range from parodies of other poets, Millay, Longfellow, Edgar Guest, Kipling, Masefield, etc., and free and hilarious translations of Horace and other Latin poets, to satiric comments on fabled American institutions—the New York Subways, preposterous ads, suburbanites, sensational journalism, etc. They reveal with vigor and clarity the humor, integrity and restraint of a wise and gentle American satirist. Introduction by Robert Hutchinson. vi + 122pp. 5⅜ x 8½.
T108 Paperbound **$1.00**

SINGULAR TRAVELS, CAMPAIGNS, AND ADVENTURES OF BARON MUNCHAUSEN, R. E. Raspe, with 90 illustrations by Gustave Doré. The first edition in over 150 years to reestablish the deeds of the Prince of Liars exactly as Raspe first recorded them in 1785—the genuine Baron Munchausen, one of the most popular personalities in English literature. Included also are the best of the many sequels, written by other hands. Introduction on Raspe by J. Carswell. Bibliography of early editions. xliv + 192pp. 5⅜ x 8.
T698 Paperbound **$1.00**

THE WIT AND HUMOR OF OSCAR WILDE, ed. by Alvin Redman. Wilde at his most brilliant, in 1000 epigrams exposing weaknesses and hypocrisies of "civilized" society. Divided into 49 categories—sin, wealth, women, America, etc.—to aid writers, speakers. Includes excerpts from his trials, books, plays, criticism. Formerly "The Epigrams of Oscar Wilde." Introduction by Vyvyan Holland, Wilde's only living son. Introductory essay by editor. 260pp. 5⅜ x 8.
T602 Paperbound **$1.00**

MAX AND MORITZ, Wilhelm Busch. Busch is one of the great humorists of all time, as well as the father of the modern comic strip. This volume, translated by H. A. Klein and other hands, contains the perennial favorite "Max and Moritz" (translated by C. T. Brooks), Plisch and Plum, Das Rabennest, Eispeter, and seven other whimsical, sardonic, jovial, diabolical cartoon and verse stories. Lively English translations parallel the original German. This work has delighted millions, since it first appeared in the 19th century, and is guaranteed to please almost anyone. Edited by H. A. Klein, with an afterword. x + 205pp. 5⅝ x 8½.
T181 Paperbound **$1.00**

HYPOCRITICAL HELENA, Wilhelm Busch. A companion volume to "Max and Moritz," with the title piece (Die Fromme Helena) and 10 other highly amusing cartoon and verse stories, all newly translated by H. A. Klein and M. C. Klein: Adventure on New Year's Eve (Abenteuer in der Neujahrsnacht), Hangover on the Morning after New Year's Eve (Der Katzenjammer am Neujahrsmorgen), etc. English and German in parallel columns. Hours of pleasure, also a fine language aid. x + 205pp. 5⅝ x 8½.
T184 Paperbound **$1.00**

THE BEAR THAT WASN'T, Frank Tashlin. What does it mean? Is it simply delightful wry humor, or a charming story of a bear who wakes up in the midst of a factory, or a satire on Big Business, or an existential cartoon-story of the human condition, or a symbolization of the struggle between conformity and the individual? New York Herald Tribune said of the first edition: ". . . a fable for grownups that will be fun for children. Sit down with the book and get your own bearings." Long an underground favorite with readers of all ages and opinions. x + 51pp. Illustrated. 5⅜ x 8½.
T939 Paperbound **75¢**

RUTHLESS RHYMES FOR HEARTLESS HOMES and MORE RUTHLESS RHYMES FOR HEARTLESS HOMES, Harry Graham ("Col. D. Streamer"). Two volumes of Little Willy and 48 other poetic disasters. A bright, new reprint of oft-quoted, never forgotten, devastating humor by a precursor of today's "sick" joke school. For connoisseurs of wicked, wacky humor and all who delight in the comedy of manners. Original drawings are a perfect complement. 61 illustrations. Index. vi + 69pp. Two vols. bound as one. 5⅜ x 8½.
T930 Paperbound **75¢**

CATALOGUE OF DOVER BOOKS

Say It language phrase books

These handy phrase books (128 to 196 pages each) make grammatical drills unnecessary for an elementary knowledge of a spoken foreign language. Covering most matters of travel and everyday life each volume contains:

Over 1000 phrases and sentences in immediately useful forms — foreign language plus English.

Modern usage designed for Americans. Specific phrases like, "Give me small change," and "Please call a taxi."

Simplified phonetic transcription you will be able to read at sight.

The only completely indexed phrase books on the market.

Covers scores of important situations: — Greetings, restaurants, sightseeing, useful expressions, etc.

These books are prepared by native linguists who are professors at Columbia, N.Y.U., Fordham and other great universities. Use them independently or with any other book or record course. They provide a supplementary living element that most other courses lack. Individual volumes in:

Russian 75¢	Italian 75¢	Spanish 75¢	German 75¢
Hebrew 75¢	Danish 75¢	Japanese 75¢	Swedish 75¢
Dutch 75¢	Esperanto 75¢	Modern Greek 75¢	Portuguese 75¢
Norwegian 75¢	Polish 75¢	French 75¢	Yiddish 75¢
Turkish 75¢		English for German-speaking people 75¢	
English for Italian-speaking people 75¢		English for Spanish-speaking people 75¢	

Large clear type. 128-196 pages each. 3½ x 5¼. Sturdy paper binding.

Listen and Learn language records

LISTEN & LEARN is the only language record course designed especially to meet your travel and everyday needs. It is available in separate sets for FRENCH, SPANISH, GERMAN, JAPANESE, RUSSIAN, MODERN GREEK, PORTUGUESE, ITALIAN and HEBREW, and each set contains three 33⅓ rpm long-playing records—1½ hours of recorded speech by eminent native speakers who are professors at Columbia, New York University, Queens College.

Check the following special features found only in LISTEN & LEARN:

- **Dual-language recording.** 812 selected phrases and sentences, over 3200 words, spoken first in English, then in their foreign language equivalents. A suitable pause follows each foreign phrase, allowing you time to repeat the expression. You learn by unconscious assimilation.

- **128 to 206-page manual** contains everything on the records, plus a simple phonetic pronunciation guide.

- **Indexed for convenience.** The only set on the market that is completely indexed. No more puzzling over where to find the phrase you need. Just look in the rear of the manual.

- **Practical.** No time wasted on material you can find in any grammar. LISTEN & LEARN covers central core material with phrase approach. Ideal for the person with limited learning time.

- **Living, modern expressions,** not found in other courses. Hygienic products, modern equipment, shopping—expressions used every day, like "nylon" and "air-conditioned."

- **Limited objective.** Everything you learn, no matter where you stop, is immediately useful. You have to finish other courses, wade through grammar and vocabulary drill, before they help you.

- **High-fidelity recording.** LISTEN & LEARN records equal in clarity and surface-silence any record on the market costing up to $6.

"Excellent . . . the spoken records . . . impress me as being among the very best on the market," **Prof. Mario Pei,** Dept. of Romance Languages, Columbia University. "Inexpensive and well-done . . . it would make an ideal present," CHICAGO SUNDAY TRIBUNE. "More genuinely helpful than anything of its kind which I have previously encountered," **Sidney Clark,** well-known author of "ALL THE BEST" travel books.

UNCONDITIONAL GUARANTEE. Try LISTEN & LEARN, then return it within 10 days for full refund if you are not satisfied.

Each set contains three twelve-inch 33⅓ records, manual, and album.

SPANISH	the set $5.95	GERMAN	the set $5.95
FRENCH	the set $5.95	ITALIAN	the set $5.95
RUSSIAN	the set $5.95	JAPANESE	the set $5.95
PORTUGUESE	the set $5.95	MODERN GREEK	the set $5.95
MODERN HEBREW	the set $5.95		

Americana

THE EYES OF DISCOVERY, J. Bakeless. A vivid reconstruction of how unspoiled America appeared to the first white men. Authentic and enlightening accounts of Hudson's landing in New York, Coronado's trek through the Southwest; scores of explorers, settlers, trappers, soldiers. America's pristine flora, fauna, and Indians in every region and state in fresh and unusual new aspects. "A fascinating view of what the land was like before the first highway went through," Time. 68 contemporary illustrations, 39 newly added in this edition. Index. Bibliography. x + 500pp. 5⅜ x 8. T761 Paperbound **$2.00**

AUDUBON AND HIS JOURNALS, J. J. Audubon. A collection of fascinating accounts of Europe and America in the early 1800's through Audubon's own eyes. Includes the Missouri River Journals —an eventful trip through America's untouched heartland, the Labrador Journals, the European Journals, the famous "Episodes", and other rare Audubon material, including the descriptive chapters from the original letterpress edition of the "Ornithological Studies", omitted in all later editions. Indispensable for ornithologists, naturalists, and all lovers of Americana and adventure. 70-page biography by Audubon's granddaughter. 38 illustrations. Index. Total of 1106pp. 5⅜ x 8. T675 Vol I Paperbound **$2.25**
T676 Vol II Paperbound **$2.25**
The set **$4.50**

TRAVELS OF WILLIAM BARTRAM, edited by Mark Van Doren. The first inexpensive illustrated edition of one of the 18th century's most delightful books is an excellent source of first-hand material on American geography, anthropology, and natural history. Many descriptions of early Indian tribes are our only source of information on them prior to the infiltration of the white man. "The mind of a scientist with the soul of a poet," John Livingston Lowes. 13 original illustrations and maps. Edited with an introduction by Mark Van Doren. 448pp. 5⅜ x 8. T13 Paperbound **$2.00**

GARRETS AND PRETENDERS: A HISTORY OF BOHEMIANISM IN AMERICA, A. Parry. The colorful and fantastic history of American Bohemianism from Poe to Kerouac. This is the only complete record of hoboes, cranks, starving poets, and suicides. Here are Pfaff, Whitman, Crane, Bierce, Pound, and many others. New chapters by the author and by H. T. Moore bring this thorough and well-documented history down to the Beatniks. "An excellent account," N. Y. Times. Scores of cartoons, drawings, and caricatures. Bibliography. Index. xxviii + 421pp. 5⅝ x 8⅜. T708 Paperbound **$1.95**

THE EXPLORATION OF THE COLORADO RIVER AND ITS CANYONS, J. W. Powell. The thrilling first-hand account of the expedition that filled in the last white space on the map of the United States. Rapids, famine, hostile Indians, and mutiny are among the perils encountered as the unknown Colorado Valley reveals its secrets. This is the only uncut version of Major Powell's classic of exploration that has been printed in the last 60 years. Includes later reflections and subsequent expedition. 250 illustrations, new map. 400pp. 5⅝ x 8⅜. T94 Paperbound **$2.00**

THE JOURNAL OF HENRY D. THOREAU, Edited by Bradford Torrey and Francis H. Allen. Henry Thoreau is not only one of the most important figures in American literature and social thought; his voluminous journals (from which his books emerged as selections and crystallizations) constitute both the longest, most sensitive record of personal internal development and a most penetrating description of a historical moment in American culture. This present set, which was first issued in fourteen volumes, contains Thoreau's entire journals from 1837 to 1862, with the exception of the lost years which were found only recently. We are reissuing it, complete and unabridged, with a new introduction by Walter Harding, Secretary of the Thoreau Society. Fourteen volumes reissued in two volumes. Foreword by Henry Seidel Canby. Total of 1888pp. 8⅜ x 12¼. T312-3 Two volume set, Clothbound **$20.00**

GAMES AND SONGS OF AMERICAN CHILDREN, collected by William Wells Newell. A remarkable collection of 190 games with songs that accompany many of them; cross references to show similarities, differences among them; variations; musical notation for 38 songs. Textual discussions show relations with folk-drama and other aspects of folk tradition. Grouped into categories for ready comparative study: Love-games, histories, playing at work, human life, bird and beast, mythology, guessing-games, etc. New introduction covers relations of songs and dances to timeless heritage of folklore, biographical sketch of Newell, other pertinent data. A good source of inspiration for those in charge of groups of children and a valuable reference for anthropologists, sociologists, psychiatrists. Introduction by Carl Withers. New indexes of first lines, games. 5⅜ x 8½. xii + 242pp. T354 Paperbound **$1.75**

Art, History of Art, Antiques, Graphic Arts, Handcrafts

ART STUDENTS' ANATOMY, E. J. Farris. Outstanding art anatomy that uses chiefly living objects for its illustrations. 71 photos of undraped men, women, children are accompanied by carefully labeled matching sketches to illustrate the skeletal system, articulations and movements, bony landmarks, the muscular system, skin, fasciae, fat, etc. 9 x-ray photos show movement of joints. Undraped models are shown in such actions as serving in tennis, drawing a bow in archery, playing football, dancing, preparing to spring and to dive. Also discussed and illustrated are proportions, age and sex differences, the anatomy of the smile, etc. 8 plates by the great early 18th century anatomic illustrator Siegfried Albinus are also included. Glossary. 158 figures, 7 in color. x + 159pp. 5⅝ x 8⅜. T744 Paperbound **$1.50**

AN ATLAS OF ANATOMY FOR ARTISTS, F Schider. A new 3rd edition of this standard text enlarged by 52 new illustrations of hands, anatomical studies by Cloquet, and expressive life studies of the body by Barcsay. 189 clear, detailed plates offer you precise information of impeccable accuracy. 29 plates show all aspects of the skeleton, with closeups of special areas, while 54 full-page plates, mostly in two colors, give human musculature as seen from four different points of view, with cutaways for important portions of the body. 14 full-page plates provide photographs of hand forms, eyelids, female breasts, and indicate the location of muscles upon models. 59 additional plates show how great artists of the past utilized human anatomy. They reproduce sketches and finished work by such artists as Michelangelo, Leonardo da Vinci, Goya, and 15 others. This is a lifetime reference work which will be one of the most important books in any artist's library. "The standard reference tool," AMERICAN LIBRARY ASSOCIATION. "Excellent," AMERICAN ARTIST. Third enlarged edition. 189 plates, 647 illustrations. xxvi + 192pp. 7⅞ x 10⅝. T241 Clothbound **$6.00**

AN ATLAS OF ANIMAL ANATOMY FOR ARTISTS, W. Ellenberger, H. Baum, H. Dittrich. The largest, richest animal anatomy for artists available in English. 99 detailed anatomical plates of such animals as the horse, dog, cat, lion, deer, seal, kangaroo, flying squirrel, cow, bull, goat, monkey, hare, and bat. Surface features are clearly indicated, while progressive beneath-the-skin pictures show musculature, tendons, and bone structure. Rest and action are exhibited in terms of musculature and skeletal structure and detailed cross-sections are given for heads and important features. The animals chosen are representative of specific families so that a study of these anatomies will provide knowledge of hundreds of related species. "Highly recommended as one of the very few books on the subject worthy of being used as an authoritative guide," DESIGN. "Gives a fundamental knowledge," AMERICAN ARTIST. Second revised, enlarged edition with new plates from Cuvier, Stubbs, etc. 288 illustrations. 153pp. 11⅜ x 9. T82 Clothbound **$6.00**

THE HUMAN FIGURE IN MOTION, Eadweard Muybridge. The largest selection in print of Muybridge's famous high-speed action photos of the human figure in motion. 4789 photographs illustrate 162 different actions: men, women, children—mostly undraped—are shown walking, running, carrying various objects, sitting, lying down, climbing, throwing, arising, and performing over 150 other actions. Some actions are shown in as many as 150 photographs each. All in all there are more than 500 action strips in this enormous volume, series shots taken at shutter speeds of as high as 1/6000th of a second! These are not posed shots, but true stopped motion. They show bone and muscle in situations that the human eye is not fast enough to capture. Earlier, smaller editions of these prints have brought $40 and more on the out-of-print market. "A must for artists," ART IN FOCUS. "An unparalleled dictionary of action for all artists," AMERICAN ARTIST. 390 full-page plates, with 4789 photographs. Printed on heavy glossy stock. Reinforced binding with headbands. xxi + 390pp. 7⅞ x 10⅝. T204 Clothbound **$10.00**

ANIMALS IN MOTION, Eadweard Muybridge. This is the largest collection of animal action photos in print. 34 different animals (horses, mules, oxen, goats, camels, pigs, cats, guanacos, lions, gnus, deer, monkeys, eagles—and 21 others) in 132 characteristic actions. The horse alone is shown in more than 40 different actions. All 3919 photographs are taken in series at speeds up to 1/6000th of a second. The secrets of leg motion, spinal patterns, head movements, strains and contortions shown nowhere else are captured. You will see exactly how a lion sets his foot down; how an elephant's knees are like a human's—and how they differ; the position of a kangaroo's legs in mid-leap; how an ostrich's head bobs; details of the flight of birds—and thousands of facets of motion only the fastest cameras can catch. Photographed from domestic animals and animals in the Philadelphia zoo, it contains neither semiposed artificial shots nor distorted telephoto shots taken under adverse conditions. Artists, biologists, decorators, cartoonists, will find this book indispensable for understanding animals in motion. "A really marvelous series of plates," NATURE (London). "The dry plate's most spectacular early use was by Eadweard Muybridge," LIFE. 3919 photographs; 380 full pages of plates. 440pp. Printed on heavy glossy paper. Deluxe binding with headbands. 7⅞ x 10⅝. T203 Clothbound **$10.00**

CATALOGUE OF DOVER BOOKS

THE AUTOBIOGRAPHY OF AN IDEA, Louis Sullivan. The pioneer architect whom Frank Lloyd Wright called "the master" reveals an acute sensitivity to social forces and values in this passionately honest account. He records the crystallization of his opinions and theories, the growth of his organic theory of architecture that still influences American designers and architects, contemporary ideas, etc. This volume contains the first appearance of 34 full-page plates of his finest architecture. Unabridged reissue of 1924 edition. New introduction by R. M. Line. Index. xiv + 335pp. 5⅜ x 8. T281 Paperbound **$2.00**

THE DRAWINGS OF HEINRICH KLEY. The first uncut republication of both of Kley's devastating sketchbooks, which first appeared in pre-World War I Germany. One of the greatest cartoonists and social satirists of modern times, his exuberant and iconoclastic fantasy and his extraordinary technique place him in the great tradition of Bosch, Breughel, and Goya, while his subject matter has all the immediacy and tension of our century. 200 drawings. viii + 128pp. 7¾ x 10¾. T24 Paperbound **$1.85**

MORE DRAWINGS BY HEINRICH KLEY. All the sketches from Leut' Und Viecher (1912) and Sammel-Album (1923) not included in the previous Dover edition of Drawings. More of the bizarre, mercilessly iconoclastic sketches that shocked and amused on their original publication. Nothing was too sacred, no one too eminent for satirization by this imaginative, individual and accomplished master cartoonist. A total of 158 illustrations. Iv + 104pp. 7¾ x 10¾. T41 Paperbound **$1.85**

PINE FURNITURE OF EARLY NEW ENGLAND, R. H. Kettell. A rich understanding of one of America's most original folk arts that collectors of antiques, interior decorators, craftsmen, woodworkers, and everyone interested in American history and art will find fascinating and immensely useful. 413 illustrations of more than 300 chairs, benches, racks, beds, cupboards, mirrors, shelves, tables, and other furniture will show all the simple beauty and character of early New England furniture. 55 detailed drawings carefully analyze outstanding pieces. "With its rich store of illustrations, this book emphasizes the individuality and varied design of early American pine furniture. It should be welcomed," ANTIQUES. 413 illustrations and 55 working drawings. 475. 8 x 10¾. T145 Clothbound **$10.00**

THE HUMAN FIGURE, J. H. Vanderpoel. Every important artistic element of the human figure is pointed out in minutely detailed word descriptions in this classic text and illustrated as well in 430 pencil and charcoal drawings. Thus the text of this book directs your attention to all the characteristic features and subtle differences of the male and female (adults, children, and aged persons), as though a master artist were telling you what to look for at each stage. 2nd edition, revised and enlarged by George Bridgman. Foreword. 430 illustrations. 143pp. 6⅛ x 9¼. T432 Paperbound **$1.50**

LETTERING AND ALPHABETS, J. A. Cavanagh. This unabridged reissue of LETTERING offers a full discussion, analysis, illustration of 89 basic hand lettering styles — styles derived from Caslons, Bodonis, Garamonds, Gothic, Black Letter, Oriental, and many others. Upper and lower cases, numerals and common signs pictured. Hundreds of technical hints on make-up, construction, artistic validity, strokes, pens, brushes, white areas, etc. May be reproduced without permission! 89 complete alphabets; 72 lettered specimens. 121pp. 9¾ x 8. T53 Paperbound **$1.25**

STICKS AND STONES, Lewis Mumford. A survey of the forces that have conditioned American architecture and altered its forms. The author discusses the medieval tradition in early New England villages; the Renaissance influence which developed with the rise of the merchant class; the classical influence of Jefferson's time; the "Mechanicsvilles" of Poe's generation; the Brown Decades; the philosophy of the Imperial facade; and finally the modern machine age. "A truly remarkable book," SAT. REV. OF LITERATURE. 2nd revised edition. 21 illustrations. xvii + 228pp. 5⅜ x 8. T202 Paperbound **$1.60**

THE STANDARD BOOK OF QUILT MAKING AND COLLECTING, Marguerite Ickis. A complete easy-to-follow guide with all the information you need to make beautiful, useful quilts. How to plan, design, cut, sew, appliqué, avoid sewing problems, use rag bag, make borders, tuft, every other aspect. Over 100 traditional quilts shown, including over 40 full-size patterns. At-home hobby for fun, profit. Index. 483 illus. 1 color plate. 287pp. 6¾ x 9½. T582 Paperbound **$2.00**

THE BOOK OF SIGNS, Rudolf Koch. Formerly $20 to $25 on the out-of-print market, now only $1.00 in this unabridged new edition! 493 symbols from ancient manuscripts, medieval cathedrals, coins, catacombs, pottery, etc. Crosses, monograms of Roman emperors, astrological, chemical, botanical, runes, housemarks, and 7 other categories. Invaluable for handicraft workers, illustrators, scholars, etc., this material may be reproduced without permission. 493 illustrations by Fritz Kredel. 104pp. 6½ x 9¼. T162 Paperbound **$1.00**

PRIMITIVE ART, Franz Boas. This authoritative and exhaustive work by a great American anthropologist covers the entire gamut of primitive art. Pottery, leatherwork, metal work, stone work, wood, basketry, are treated in detail. Theories of primitive art, historical depth in art history, technical virtuosity, unconscious levels of patterning, symbolism, styles, literature, music, dance, etc. A must book for the interested layman, the anthropologist, artist, handicrafter (hundreds of unusual motifs), and the historian. Over 900 illustrations (50 ceramic vessels, 12 totem poles, etc.). 376pp. 5⅜ x 8. T25 Paperbound **$2.00**

Fiction

FLATLAND, E. A. Abbott. A science-fiction classic of life in a 2-dimensional world that is also a first-rate introduction to such aspects of modern science as relativity and hyperspace. Political, moral, satirical, and humorous overtones have made FLATLAND fascinating reading for thousands. 7th edition. New introduction by Banesh Hoffmann. 16 illustrations. 128pp. 5⅜ x 8. T1 Paperbound **$1.00**

THE WONDERFUL WIZARD OF OZ, L. F. Baum. Only edition in print with all the original W. W. Denslow illustrations in full color—as much a part of "The Wizard" as Tenniel's drawings are of "Alice in Wonderland." "The Wizard" is still America's best-loved fairy tale, in which, as the author expresses it, "The wonderment and joy are retained and the heartaches and nightmares left out." Now today's young readers can enjoy every word and wonderful picture of the original book. New introduction by Martin Gardner. A Baum bibliography. 23 full-page color plates. viii + 268pp. 5⅜ x 8. T691 Paperbound **$1.45**

THE MARVELOUS LAND OF OZ, L. F. Baum. This is the equally enchanting sequel to the "Wizard," continuing the adventures of the Scarecrow and the Tin Woodman. The hero this time is a little boy named Tip, and all the delightful Oz magic is still present. This is the Oz book with the Animated Saw-Horse, the Woggle-Bug, and Jack Pumpkinhead. All the original John R. Neill illustrations, 10 in full color. 287 pp. 5⅜ x 8. T692 Paperbound **$1.45**

FIVE GREAT DOG NOVELS, edited by Blanche Cirker. The complete original texts of five classic dog novels that have delighted and thrilled millions of children and adults throughout the world with their stories of loyalty, adventure, and courage. Full texts of Jack London's "The Call of the Wild"; John Brown's "Rab and His Friends"; Alfred Ollivant's "Bob, Son of Battle"; Marshall Saunders's "Beautiful Joe"; and Ouida's "A Dog of Flanders." 21 Illustrations from the original editions. 495pp. 5⅜ x 8. T777 Paperbound **$1.75**

TO THE SUN? and OFF ON A COMET!, Jules Verne. Complete texts of two of the most imaginative flights into fancy in world literature display the high adventure that have kept Verne's novels read for nearly a century. Only unabridged edition of the best translation, by Edward Roth. Large, easily readable type. 50 illustrations selected from first editions. 462pp. 5⅜ x 8. T634 Paperbound **$1.75**

FROM THE EARTH TO THE MOON and ALL AROUND THE MOON, Jules Verne. Complete editions of 2 of Verne's most successful novels, in finest Edward Roth translations, now available after many years out of print. Verne's visions of submarines, airplanes, television, rockets, interplanetary travel; of scientific and not-so-scientific beliefs; of peculiarities of Americans; all delight and engross us today as much as when they first appeared. Large, easily readable type. 42 illus. from first French edition. 476pp. 5⅜ x 8. T633 Paperbound **$1.75**

THE CRUISE OF THE CACHALOT, Frank T. Bullen. Out of the experiences of many years on the high-seas, First Mate Bullen created this novel of adventure aboard an American whaler, shipping out of New Bedford, Mass., when American whaling was at the height of its splendor. Originally published in 1899, the story of the round-the-world cruise of the "Cachalot" in pursuit of the sperm whale has thrilled generations of readers. A maritime classic that will fascinate anyone interested in reading about the sea or looking for a solid old-fashioned yarn, while the vivid recreation of a brief but important chapter of Americana and the British author's often biting commentary on nineteenth-century Yankee mores offer insights into the colorful era of America's coming of age. 8 plates. xiii + 271pp. 5⅜ x 8½. T774 Paperbound **$1.00**

28 SCIENCE FICTION STORIES OF H. G. WELLS. Two full unabridged novels, MEN LIKE GODS and STAR BEGOTTEN, plus 26 short stories by the master science-fiction writer of all time! Stories of space, time, invention, exploration, future adventure—an indispensable part of the library of everyone interested in science and adventure. PARTIAL CONTENTS: Men Like Gods, The Country of the Blind, In the Abyss, The Crystal Egg, The Man Who Could Work Miracles, A Story of the Days to Come, The Valley of Spiders, and 21 more! 928pp. 5⅜ x 8. T265 Clothbound **$4.50**

DAVID HARUM, E. N. Westcott. This novel of one of the most lovable, humorous characters in American literature is a prime example of regional humor. It continues to delight people who like their humor dry, their characters quaint, and their plots ingenuous. First book edition to contain complete novel plus chapter found after author's death. Illustrations from first illustrated edition. 192pp. 5⅜ x 8. T580 Paperbound **$1.15**

GESTA ROMANORUM, trans. by Charles Swan, ed. by Wynnard Hooper. 181 tales of Greeks, Romans, Britons, Biblical characters, comprise one of greatest medieval story collections, source of plots for writers including Shakespeare, Chaucer, Gower, etc. Imaginative tales of wars, incest, thwarted love, magic, fantasy, allegory, humor, tell about kings, prostitutes, philosophers, fair damsels, knights, Noah, pirates, all walks, stations of life. Introduction. Notes. 500pp. 5⅜ x 8. T535 Paperbound **$1.85**

Music

A GENERAL HISTORY OF MUSIC, Charles Burney. A detailed coverage of music from the Greeks up to 1789, with full information on all types of music: sacred and secular, vocal and instrumental, operatic and symphonic. Theory, notation, forms, instruments, innovators, composers, performers, typical and important works, and much more in an easy, entertaining style. Burney covered much of Europe and spoke with hundreds of authorities and composers so that this work is more than a compilation of records . . . it is a living work of careful and first-hand scholarship. Its account of thoroughbass (18th century) Italian music is probably still the best introduction on the subject. A recent NEW YORK TIMES review said, "Surprisingly few of Burney's statements have been invalidated by modern research . . . still of great value." Edited and corrected by Frank Mercer. 35 figures. Indices. 1915pp. 5⅜ x 8. 2 volumes. **T36 The Set, Clothbound $12.50**

A DICTIONARY OF HYMNOLOGY, John Julian. This exhaustive and scholarly work has become known as an invaluable source of hundreds of thousands of important and often difficult to obtain facts on the history and use of hymns in the western world. Everyone interested in hymns will be fascinated by the accounts of famous hymns and hymn writers and amazed by the amount of practical information he will find. More than 30,000 entries on individual hymns, giving authorship, date and circumstances of composition, publication, textual variations, translations, denominational and ritual usage, etc. Biographies of more than 9,000 hymn writers, and essays on important topics such as Christmas carols and children's hymns, and much other unusual and valuable information. A 200 page double-columned index of first lines — the largest in print. Total of 1786 pages in two reinforced clothbound volumes. 6¼ x 9¼. **The set, T333 Clothbound $17.50**

MUSIC IN MEDIEVAL BRITAIN, F. Ll. Harrison. The most thorough, up-to-date, and accurate treatment of the subject ever published, beautifully illustrated. Complete account of institutions and choirs; carols, masses, and motets; liturgy and plainsong; and polyphonic music from the Norman Conquest to the Reformation. Discusses the various schools of music and their reciprocal influences; the origin and development of new ritual forms; development and use of instruments; and new evidence on many problems of the period. Reproductions of scores, over 200 excerpts from medieval melodies. Rules of harmony and dissonance; influence of Continental styles; great composers (Dunstable, Cornysh, Fairfax, etc.); and much more. Register and index of more than 400 musicians. Index of titles. General Index. 225-item bibliography. 6 Appendices. xix + 491pp. 5⅝ x 8¾. **T705 Clothbound $10.00**

THE MUSIC OF SPAIN, Gilbert Chase. Only book in English to give concise, comprehensive account of Iberian music; new Chapter covers music since 1941. Victoria, Albéniz, Cabezón, Pedrell, Turina, hundreds of other composers; popular and folk music; the Gypsies; the guitar; dance, theatre, opera, with only extensive discussion in English of the Zarzuela; virtuosi such as Casals; much more. "Distinguished . . . readable," Saturday Review. 400-item bibliography. Index. 27 photos. 383pp. 5⅜ x 8. **T549 Paperbound $2.00**

ON STUDYING SINGING, Sergius Kagen. An intelligent method of voice-training, which leads you around pitfalls that waste your time, money, and effort. Exposes rigid, mechanical systems, baseless theories, deleterious exercises. "Logical, clear, convincing . . . dead right," Virgil Thomson, N.Y. Herald Tribune. "I recommend this volume highly," Maggie Teyte, Saturday Review. 119pp. 5⅜ x 8. **T622 Paperbound $1.25**

Prices subject to change without notice.

Dover publishes books on art, music, philosophy, literature, languages, history, social sciences, psychology, handcrafts, orientalia, puzzles and entertainments, chess, pets and gardens, books explaining science, intermediate and higher mathematics, mathematical physics, engineering, biological sciences, earth sciences, classics of science, etc. Write to:

Dept. catrr.
Dover Publications, Inc.
180 Varick Street, N.Y. 14, N.Y.